D1011424

INNOVATION
IN BIG BUSINESS

INNOVATION
IN BIG BUSINESS

Lowell W. Steele

Corporate Research and Development
General Electric Company
Schenectady, New York

ELSEVIER
New York/Oxford/Amsterdam

AMERICAN ELSEVIER PUBLISHING COMPANY, INC.
52 Vanderbilt Avenue, New York, N.Y. 10017

ELSEVIER PUBLISHING COMPANY
335 Jan Van Galenstraat, P.O. Box 211
Amsterdam, The Netherlands

© American Elsevier Publishing Co., Inc. 1975.   All rights reserved.
No part of this publication may be reproduced,
stored in a retrieval system, or transmitted
in any form or by any means, electronic,
mechanical, photocopying, recording,
or otherwise, without permission in
writing from the publisher.
American Elsevier Publishing Company, Inc.
52 Vanderbilt Avenue, New York, N.Y. 10017.

Library of Congress Cataloging in Publication Data

Steele, Lowell W
  Innovation in big business.

  Includes bibliographical references.
  1. Technological innovations. 2. Research,
Industrial—Management. I. Title.
HD45.S754   658.5'7   75-14971
ISBN 0-444-00170-0 (Amer. Elsevier)
ISBN 0-7204-8600-9 (North-Holland)

Manufactured in the United States of America.

658.57
S814i

193835

Contents

MILLS COLLEGE
LIBRARY

Preface

The emergence of research and development(R&D) as a major industrial and economic activity is one of the most noteworthy phenomena of the post-World War II era. As such it has attracted much attention and has been studied extensively. This interest probably peaked in the late 1960s, a period which in so many ways marked the end of an era. A new perspective is needed of both the past and the future. Such a perspective is very difficult to establish during a period of rapid change and is likely to have dubious validity even if possible. But the in-between times, the periods of transition, are the times to reexamine postulates, to gain new understanding of what has been happening, and to forecast where we seem to be headed.

Most of the earlier attention to R&D focused on that activity as an isolated entity. The customers, the clients, the sponsors, the context in which R&D functioned remained largely in the shadows. The participants in David Allison's R&D game were caught up in the pressure cooker of adolescent growth—conscious of internal functioning, of the need to establish identity and to carve out one's place in the sun.

This book focuses on context. R&D is not an isolated activity; it is not an end in itself. Its role in, and relationship with, the larger industrial context must be better understood if its lusty adolescent growth is to be followed by sustained adult performance.

It has become obvious that the crucial problems in the management of research and development are at the interface between the R&D organization and its sponsor or those who use its outputs. These problems loom largest in the eyes of R&D managers; they dominate their conversations. The problems can be grouped under two broad questions: Are we working on the right technical problems with the appropriate allocation of effort? *and* How can we get the outputs of R&D used? I am shifting the perspective from the parochial view inside the R&D organization looking out—even looking out at its own interface—and instead am seeking to get out on the interface itself to try to understand the viewpoints on both sides. One consequence of this approach is that part of what I have to say will seem simple-minded and obvious to the professionals on either side. Nevertheless, this alternative appraisal has remained latent to date in most discussions of R&D management.

The book is thus aimed at two principal industrial audiences as well as at students in engineering and business administration. First is that group of R&D managers who are concerned with improving the effectiveness and viability of the R&D component, and thus improving its coupling with, and contribution to, the sponsoring organization. The second group comprises the general managers who must make the resource allocation decisions that support R&D and who must wrestle with the complex problems of formulating the role of technology for their businesses and of obtaining the technology inputs they need for their operations. The subject of the management of technology is emerging as a desirable field of study in the engineering curriculum and in business administration. Consequently, I hope that this book will stimulate additional interest in the subject and that students in the field will find it helpful.

The perspective throughout is that of achieving effective coupling with the sponsoring business enterprise. We will examine the role of R&D as it has evolved, the environment for innovation, problems of determining the role of technology in business strategy and of determining the R&D inputs needed for that strategy. We will also look at the transition of R&D outputs to commercial application and at communication with operating people. Finally, we will turn toward the future and consider the management of temporary organizations and the special problems of conducting R&D in a multinational framework. The typical management problems associated with the internal operation of a laboratory are not addressed, since these areas have already received extensive coverage in the literature.

Every author's insights and judgments are formed by interactions with a multitude of people, most of whom are anonymous even to him. I have had the good fortune to participate in thousands of formal interviews and informal conversations with scientists and engineers who as a class comprise one of the world's most challenging, stimulating, and sometimes provoking groups of people. Inevitably, by virtue of propinquity, temperament, and capability, some stand out. Of the many names that come to mind, John Bragg, Art Bueche, Malcolm Hebb, Stan Neal, and Roland Schmitt warrant special mention.

I have particularly benefited from the comments of David Allison of Xerox, S. W. Davidson (retired) of Eastman Kodak, L. L. Ferguson (retired) of General Electric, and Frank Persons (retired) of Esso Research & Engineering in reviewing the manuscript.

I owe an especial note of gratitude to the General Electric Company, whose diverse business interests, deep involvement in technology, and tradition of technical leadership have provided the basis for much of my understanding of industrial R&D and innovation. I hasten to add that the book is not an exposition of General Electric policies and modes of operation. I am solely responsible for the validity of the conclusions and analyses contained herein. It goes without saying that I am also responsible for errors of fact and deficiencies in logic or in clarity of exposition.

Mrs. Evelyn Gejay has retained her composure and good humor while retyping innumerable drafts and deciphering my hieroglyphics.

My wife Jean and my children Bob, Cindy, Dave, and Andy have accepted the diversion of my time and energy with unfailing patience and unflagging support and enthusiasm. I am profoundly grateful for their help and understanding.

—*Lowell W. Steele*

Introduction

This is a book about the management of change in large companies. More particularly, it is about improving the effectiveness of research and development as one of the principal instruments for generating change. Whether we like it or not, we live in a world of giant institutions in all segments of our society. In the economic sphere, with a gross national product of over one trillion dollars, a labor force of over 80 million people, and with a situation in which international trade is essentially competition among governments, we all have a stake in maintaining the effectiveness and viability of the great national and international firms that are the heart of our industrial system. Events of recent years have demonstrated the shock waves generated when a large company founders or gets into serious trouble.

Maintaining the capacity for change is an indispensable feature of the ability to survive. In a changing world the organization that cannot respond faces the disastrous fate of the dinosaur. Yet the social events of the past decade remind all of us that change—even necessary and desirable change—is a painful process. The creation of the new seems to require the destruction and restructuring of the old. Thus, change is threatening. Perceptions of whether change is in fact necessary, whether it is pointed in the right direction, and whether it is being implemented effectively will vary widely among those who are affected. Because of the threat involved in the change, these differences will be expressed with great force. Consequently, mechanisms to assure an adequate degree of change will be difficult to establish and maintain. One is in effect trying to modulate a process that traditionally has proceeded in bursts when pent-up forces break their bounds.

The growth of technology is itself creating a requirement to deal with change more effectively. All of society is going through an expansion of the time/space dimensions in which human thought and action occur. We have a much better data base with which to work, a data base that not only gives us a better grasp of the immediate world in which we live, but also greatly enlarges the dimensions of the "world" that becomes relevant within the limits of our consideration. We also have greater ability to manipulate and to simulate different possible future worlds through the use of the computer and of model building. Thus, we have the capacity to accommodate a larger universe of variables in our considerations. A responsible management must attempt to assess the implications of this larger universe for the future of the enterprise. In effect, management's sphere of accountability for insuring the future viability of the corporation is being enlarged.

And, finally, the accelerating rate of change is also forcing more attention to the task of trying to predict the future. In older, simpler times the future was likely to be very much like the present, so there was little to be gained from trying to predict it more precisely. We now are becoming increasingly aware of the tyranny of geometric growth, of the fact that even relatively small changes, if they persist over a long period of time, can accumulate to a very large consequence. We are shifting more attention from a study of history to the prediction of the future. This is true with respect to population trends, with respect to environment and world resources, and with respect to the structure and values of society.

In the face of this growing concern over the need to respond to a changing environment and of the broadened time/space perspective in which it is exercised, the clear moral directive for every large organization is: "Learn how to change effectively or die." The question the organization must answer is: "What can be done to reduce the trauma, to minimize the dysfunctional features involved in change, and to reduce the errors made in introducing change?"

Scientists have always looked for a model system to study when they are exploring a new area of nature. They look for a system that is relevant to the question they wish to answer and yet which is simple enough to be amenable to study. Frequently, the real world is far too complicated to be studied directly. While it may seem ridiculous, I am proposing that the large corporation is in fact an attractive model system for studying the process of change. A moment's thought will conclude that these corporations do have some valuable advantages for such a study. First, in comparison with most other very large institutions, the corporation has relatively clear objectives that are traditional—to grow and to produce a satisfactory return to the shareowners. Thus, its degree of success can be ascertained relatively unambiguously. Second, a great deal of thought has been given to the functional role of the various components that comprise the operation of these great enterprises. We know a lot about what they contribute to the organization and what skills they require. Third, the structure of the organization, particularly in the large corporation, is typically quite carefully delineated in an anatomical sense, with the various components identified and their roles and relationships specified. Because of this specification of functions and structure, changes are identifiable with relative ease. Fourth, since industrial enterprises have been subject to laws, regulation, and political and social pressures for decades, they have generated a substantial body of experience in responding to a changing environment. Finally, the large corporation, in contrast to many organizations, has relatively extensive records of its past activities, of its plans, and of its accomplishments against plans. As a consequence, the results of its operations are more clearly established and the methodologies by which its records are kept are generally well-accepted conventions throughout industry. Thus, giant companies are perhaps more amenable to study; yet they are sufficiently complex that the insights derived may have broader applicability.

Within this general framework of using very large corporations as a vehicle for understanding the generation of change, research and development is a particularly fruitful area for investigation because it has long been identified with the generation of change. Economic forecasters are always pleased if they can identify a leading indicator, some variable or combination of varibles in our economic system which move in advance of more general change and therefore give a signal of impending change elsewhere in the economy. R&D has long been recognized as a major instrument of change in society with consequences that affect all aspects of our lives. It may also be fruitful to regard research and development as a leading indicator in the general area of the organization and management of change in large corporations. In many important respects the managers of research and development have long been contending with precisely this problem.

The success of R&D components is almost uniquely dependent on their ability to induce client organizations to modify their objectives or their behavior. Furthermore, they deal more or less routinely with a number of features that, it is said, will increasingly be characteristic of all large corporations: the management of a large cadre of professional people, increased reliance on project management, use of temporary organizations that are created for special limited-purpose objectives and then dissolved, and growing need for a highly efficient network of informal communication which is required to maintain effective operation in the face of a large degree of uncertainty. Consequently, better understanding of the management of research and development may also prove useful to business managers more generally because the lessons learned in this relative microcosm can be applied advantageously in other components of the enterprise or to the corporation in its totality.

Most R&D management studies focus on the internal functioning of the R&D organization. They probe such questions as how to stimulate the creativity of the professional staff, how to improve the process of project selection and project management, and how to insure appropriate compensation for professional people. The perspective is focused inward on the operation of the R&D organization itself or is directed toward the viewpoints of the R&D group as they relate to the external world. This is a curiously isolated view, which leads to parochial insights. It has tended to reinforce an attitude of "we and they," which is characteristic of many research and development people in industry.

Ten years ago, after completing an extensive study of the utilization of senior technical people and of the extent to which they were achieving the satisfactions they had sought in working in industrial research, I commented that for an activity which seemed to be the darling of the public's eye and which was enjoying an unprecedented rate of growth nationally, R&D people were curiously on the defensive. Many regarded their activities as not well understood by the management that controlled their financial support, and they felt that their function was therefore vulnerable. They did not see themselves as an integral part of the ongoing processes that comprise the operation of the business. They took a "we and they" attitude.

Some professionals in R&D may find the emphasis on context, on the interplay between R&D and the rest of the enterprise, to be disconcerting. This broader focus inevitably disparages to some extent the special character of R&D. I hope that many will be reassured by what I intend as a more balanced perspective, which seeks to incorporate R&D into the mainstream of operations rather than keeping it a thing apart. A "we and they" viewpoint is an attitude that has outlived its usefulness.

This book represents a distillation of 20 years' experience in a major industrial laboratory, supplemented by extensive interactions with R&D organizations throughout the United States, Europe, and Japan. Although my experience is principally associated with General Electric, and I have benefited enormously from that association, I am not providing an exposition of the policies and practices in General Electric. My colleagues may not necessarily agree with every concept I am advocating. Many of my insights have been generated by comparing the approaches we were using with those being used by other major companies. Moreover, General Electric is itself so diverse that it provides opportunity to study a wide variety of approaches to the use of technology in a business and of the ways to obtain the R&D inputs needed by a business.

I have sought to avoid preparing a handbook for management. The emphasis is on a way of perceiving the context in which R&D operates and on providing a taxonomy for thought and analysis. I believe strongly that the particular methodologies used in managing a research and development organization must be home-grown in order to be effective. This position is not popular. All managers keep hoping that there is an easy way out, that somebody can hand them a set of methodologies which they simply have to manipulate in order to manage the operation. I advocate the principle that in many management activities most of the benefit results from the processes reequired to perform the work, not in the results produced. In particular, the priorities, prejudices, and capabilities of the local management are crucial ingredients in the introduction and operation of any methodological management system, and these priorities and prejudices must become manifest and be reflected in the system if it is to work effectively. And they will become so only if the management has itself gone through the time-consuming, frustrating, and provocative task of trying to develop its own methodologies. Nevertheless, it does help to have a place to start, and this book attempts to provide that place by suggesting a point of view, a way of thinking about research and development and its role in the corporate enterprise, and a way of approaching the coupling problems with which R&D must deal effectively if it is to achieve its ultimate goal.

The management of change obviously affects all functions—a point to be elaborated subsequently. Nevertheless, R&D has an almost exclusive association with the creation of change. Thus, discovering ways to improve the management of R&D represents, from the corporate point of view, a key step in increasing the capability of the entire organization to generate constructive change. Out of such new direction comes the self-renewal that maintains the vitality and viability crucial to large corporations if they are to continue to warrant their birthright.

1   Can We Institutionalize the Creation of Change?

Maybe it is just in the nature of things for R&D to be full of paradoxes. Even its historical roots appear incompatible. On the one hand, it has strong ties to the academic tradition with its emphasis on contemplative work, the high value it places on cognitive processes, and the acquisition of understanding. On the other hand, R&D's ancestry is also that of the inventor-entrepreneur who brings change, upset, and controversy along with him and who frequently proceeds intuitively.

For whatever reasons, one would have to regard the present state of R&D as a strange mixture of the favorable and the adverse. For the past 25 years, R&D has been a favored activity—socially, economically, and politically. The professions of science and engineering have been accorded high social status. Furthermore, leading scientists and engineers have had high visibility on the national scene and have been included among the savants of our society. Through a combination of governmental and industrial action, R&D has been one of the most favored sectors of our economy. It grew from 1.43% of gross national product (GNP) in 1953 to a maximum of 2.98% in 1967, an annual growth rate of 10.2%. Since then it has been growing at 4.5%, which means virtually a constant level of effort after allowance for inflation. Strength and effectiveness in R&D have come to be accepted as critical ingredients in national strength, welfare, and security. Thus, manipulation of R&D as an explicit instrument of governmental policy is virtually universal among developed countries. Perhaps most important is the fact that R&D has come to be regarded as the genie in the bottle which will provide all mankind with the means to achieve its desires and as essential for dealing with undesired and unforeseen consequences such as the current widespread problems of pollution, lower mortality rates, and increased longevity.

In jarring contrast to these favorable factors are the many indications that R&D is also in trouble nationally. Morale among academic technical faculties has been characterized as lower than at any time since World War II. Governmental expenditures on R&D actually decreased from $15 billion in 1968 to $14.7 billion in 1970 and then resumed a slight upward trend. Critics in Congress have become increasingly vocal in questioning the internal administration of R&D and the level of expenditures devoted to it. This questioning of national priorities includes not only concern over whether R&D itself is focusing on the right objectives (e.g., space research vs. transportation, health, or pollution), but also whether expenditures on other types of efforts instead of R&D might not be more productive.

While the rate of growth of total expenditures in industry had been relatively constant until the recession of 1970–1971, discussions among R&D people and in the press indicate a growing group of skeptics among American businessmen, who are wondering whether their investment in R&D has produced adequate return.

Perhaps unkindest of all, rather than being regarded as one of mankind's great benefactors, R&D is increasingly regarded by many as a monster that has befouled our world, recklessly wasted earth's scarce resources, and created disruptive change faster than civilization can absorb it.

Sources of Present Problems in R&D

In part, R&D is a victim of its own success. Its very rate of growth has greatly increased its visibility. Thus, its strengths and weaknesses, its achievements and lapses are much more subject to debate. Even more, the fact that it is considered so important to social and economic well-being means that its performance *must* be debated—it is too important to ignore. Since it has come to be regarded as a powerful engine for generating change, the question of what kind of change—R&D for what objectives—becomes a very important one for society to debate. Furthermore, as an economic activity representing about 2.3% of GNP and expending $32 billion, its objectives, responsiveness, and effectiveness must be examined carefully.

Moreover, it has long been apparent that the rate of change that persisted for 20 years cannot be maintained. No sector of the economy can grow indefinitely at twice the national average. Inevitably, any decrease in the slope of its growth curve after such a long period will be perceived, at least temporarily, as a major change in fortune for many practitioners and will cause concern over the future vitality of R&D.

By the same token, an extended period of rapid growth in itself generates an accumulation of problems that increasingly burden the system and which eventually must be resolved or ameliorated in some fashion. Society's expectations of R&D have been to some degree simplistic, with little appreciation of the difficulty of the task or of the time and effort required to achieve it. Many have, unfortunately, come to believe that R&D can do anything *now*. In part, work of this type has been debased by indiscriminate labeling, with all manner of dubious activities being identified as R&D and all manner of questionable achievements being tagged as its product. Clearly, the nontechnical layman needs to acquire a more realistic appreciation of what R&D can contribute, of the time scale in which it operates, and of the environment in which it flourishes.

A group of problems which is perhaps less palatable arises from the attitudes that inevitably emerge during a long period of prosperity in any sector of our economy. It is exceedingly difficult for people to maintain continuing critical appraisal of both their priorities and their own effectiveness as researchers during a long period of sustained and rapid growth. Consequently, R&D has not escaped the accumulation of an increasing number of practitioners whose standards do not measure up to the traditions of the profession; even more serious is that it has accumulated a large momentum on work chosen by criteria that in many cases have not been, critically reexamined for a long time. This latter point is particularly important with respect to the relationship between R&D and society. Some of the exceedingly critical comments being expressed now arise from a genuine belief that the social and economic objectives to which R&D has contributed have not necessarily been wisely chosen or at least have not reflected a proper balance in serving the needs of our society. But some derogation undoubtedly also arises from a belief that scientists and engineers have in fact not been adequately responsive to the expressed needs of society, but rather have been too inclined to decide for themselves what society should get from its investment in science and technology. The findings of the Rothschild[17] report in Great Britain, which asserted that all applied research should be required to have a specific sponsor, certainly reflect this belief.

Creating a New Institution

Many of these difficulties can, I believe, be traced to the inevitable time lag that exists between a rapidly changing social structure and values on the one hand and on people's perceptions of, and capacity to modify, their behavior in response to those events on the other. Prior to World War II, R&D was a small activity with a tradition of relatively loose coupling with society and with low profile visibility. This is not to say that the prewar outputs of research were not demonstrably worthwhile. Advances in radio and television, air transportation, polymer chemistry, and medicine were dramatically evident. Nevertheless, its practitioners were generally regarded as esoteric specialists who pursued the occult, who were divorced from practical affairs. But from the point of view of society it didn't make much difference, because they weren't paid very well; they didn't, in total, represent any significant investment of our available resources; and their contributions were regarded as vaguely useful in some abstract, diffuse, long-term kind of way. True, their work was not understandable, and their modes of behavior and discourse frequently departed from the social norm, but they could be tolerated with little difficulty.

World War II changed all that. It suddenly turned out that what these people did or were capable of doing had enormous potential for good or for harm. This revelation came somewhat as a shock to both members of the profession and society at large. Not surprisingly, the leaders of the profession—scientists and engineers—in industry, government, and the academic community became advocates, outspoken and effective ones, for the role of science and technology in our society and for the desirability of diverting increasing portions of our national resources to this kind of activity.

In effect, what we have been doing is creating a new social function; we are creating a new institution for the generation of change. The creation or the destruction of a social institution is always rather awe inspiring, but it is particularly so when the function of the new institution is itself to create change on a continuing purposive basis.

Creating social institutions takes time, lots of time. We begin to acquire our familiarity with our social institutions at an early age. We learn the roles and statuses of its practitioners—teachers, lawyers, ministers, politicians, businessmen—and our relationship to them; we learn enough of the language to permit valid discourse between ourselves and the members; we learn of and come to accept the contributions of these institutions to our society; we learn of the relationships among institutions in our social structure. All these interrelations, and more, become part of the world we live in and part of the social order we perceive. The order thus created provides predictability in social responses and a subconscious reassurance that we understand how our social world works and can participate in it effectively.

Creating a new institution or significantly modifying the role of an old one requires a redistribution of resources and a restructuring of relationships, which are unlikely to occur without conflict. This situation is true on a macroscale when we look at society as a whole, and it is also true on a microscale when we look at the creation of a new function in industry or in a particular firm. First, the role of this new institution (function) must come to be defined and accepted, whether it involves a reshuffling of activities previously distributed among several other institutions (or functions, if we are looking at a firm) or whether it represents the creation of new activities and new objectives not previously sought. Second, the relationship, the nature of the interface between this new institution and other institutions (or functions), must be worked out and come to be generally accepted by other members of society (or of the enterprise). What is the relationship among scientists and engineers and humanists as spokesmen for our times? What is the relationship between R&D and the educational structure of our society, between R&D and medicine, R&D and the church, R&D and government? What is the role of R&D in the crucial battles that define and redefine the purposes of society, that establish objectives, specify means to be employed for achieving ends, establish priorities. In short, what relationships determine the pecking order of power in society?

At the microlevel, when examining the effect on the internal operations of a business by creating a new function, one also encounters a need to generate a whole new set of relationships: For example, what is the relationship of R&D to marketing with respect to product planning; to manufacturing with respect to the introduction of new materials or new processes; even to finance with respect to estimates of costs and of levels of investment required? Just as in society as a whole, the insertion of a new function in a business necessitates a reshuffling of the power structure.

The Role of Advocates

It follows that these complex processes involve subtle learning and accommodation by human beings, which to a substantial extent defy formal efforts to systematize. This learning is acquired principally from experience and observation rather than from precept. It also follows that an event such as the creation of a new institution is not likely to occur unless society is to a considerable extent receptive to the undertaking and, just as important, unless the fledgling institution is the fortunate beneficiary of some exceedingly effective advocacy.

R&D has needed advocates, able people believing passionately in its destiny, deeply committed to furthering its cause, ambitious to make their mark on the world in this arena—and R&D has had such advocates. To some degree, recognition and acceptance of a new institution are given by the members of a society as they become familiar with its contribution; to some extent, recognition is commanded by the way in which the fledgling behaves and the contribution it in fact makes; and to some extent, recognition is demanded by the pioneering advocates of the institution—it muscles its way in.

The role of advocates (in their extreme political form we call them revolutionaries) is a fascinating one. By definition, an advocate's posture, his method of addressing a problem or situation, must be one-sided. He is committed to changing the course of events toward a new direction; therefore, an even-handed balanced approach is unlikely. By the same token his posture must be one of separation, if not of alienation, from the institutions and values at issue. His task is to state the case for change as forcefully and effectively as he can and leave the exercise of judgment up to others. The full subtlety and range of this role is perhaps most visibly elaborated in our courts through the role of lawyers as advocates in a ritualized adversary process.

Accommodating to New Realities

However, just as with revolutionaries who must adopt new modes of behavior when their success places them in the position of having to govern rather than to revolt, it seems likely that practitioners of an advocacy for R&D—having succeeded in creating a new institution—must learn to adopt new modes of behavior, must acquire new perceptions of the relationship of R&D to society or to a particular firm. The work involved in achieving effective integration and smooth working relationships with other institutions or functions differs significantly from that of forcing one's way into the game.

As the earlier discussion indicates, in many ways R&D has arrived: It has achieved a substantial reallocation of resources, it has attracted and trained the human resources to carry out its role, and, perhaps most important, it has demonstrated by its contributions that it can give to society the indispensable wherewithal for human betterment. However, as I noted earlier, I am struck by the extent to which people in R&D are still defensive; they tend to adopt a "we and they" outlook in viewing the rest of society or the rest of the enterprise, or Congress. They tend to perpetuate some of the folklore that has grown up with respect to the conditions needed for effective R&D and the manner in which its practitioners must be treated; or they refuse to reexamine for themselves the continued need for the special treatment and protective mechanisms that were absolutely mandatory for the fledgling institution (function) but which may no longer be needed and in fact may be dysfunctional.

The thing that makes this entire sequence of events so fascinating and so terribly important is the truly revolutionary character of what R&D people were trying to do—to institutionalize the process of change itself. The very concept is a contradiction! To institutionalize means to create a place for, to build in, to internalize, to make seem familiar and natural. How can change—intrinsically disruptive, creating controversy and anxiety, forcing unfamiliar relationships and strange terminology—be institutionalized? Is it possible to create a viable institution for the express purpose of generating and implementing change? I don't know the answer to this question, but we are already well along with the experiment. This book is an attempt to look at some aspects of this undertaking, using the large industrial enterprise as the vehicle for the examination. The focus on large corporations should not mislead one into the erroneous conclusion that the collective impact of the thousands of other enterprises participating in R&D is negligible. R&D results of major import have come from small efforts as well as large ones (some, indeed, would argue that the small effort is more likely to be productive of major advances). Nevertheless, R&D is an activity in which large corporations dominate. In the United States 19% of all industrial R&D is performed by just 4 companies and over 75% is performed by only 100 companies. Thus, such firms constitute a nontrivial aspect of the problem. Furthermore, they may be regarded as a microcosm whose greater coherence and simplicity may permit analysis and foster insights that are applicable to society as a whole.

2

Contrasting Approaches to Innovation

The process of creating change is now generally denoted by the use of the term "innovation." What is innovation in industry really like? How does it get done? How can it be made more effective? These are questions that must be given better answers, and the answers must be incorporated more effectively into operating procedures if the institutionalization of change is in fact going to fulfill its potential. R&D managers consistently emphasize the difficulty of introducing innovations into the business. "How do you accomplish the 'commercialization of new products'?" is a universal question. Apparently the knowledge and skill associated with successful innovation are not acquired by osmosis. It is commonplace that certain divisions of a company are frequently much more dedicated to and successful at innovation than others and that these differences persist for years without any apparent intrinsic differences in the relative opportunity for innovation. Thus, it is apparent that examination of innovation must include the total enterprise and not just the R&D component. The next three chapters will explore different facets of this problem. In this chapter we explore two different kinds of innovation and the role each plays in a business. In Chapter 3 we will examine the general institutional milieu in a large company with respect to its conduciveness to innovation and in Chapter 4 the general organizational requirements for achieving successful innovation. And finally, in Chapter 5 we will explore some of the specific features of the general managerial climate that are necessary to foster innovation.

As Donald Schon[34] has pointed out, the process of innovation is disruptive and creates uncertainty. It can almost look like a battle, and to the inventor all the rest of the people downstream may look like the enemy. Their failure to pursue their work with adequate zeal, diligence, and skill can spell the end of his creation.

The fact that innovation is a process of which R&D is only a part, and even of which all technical work is only a part, is not well enough recognized, particularly among technical people. In fact, it is in all probability better recognized by general management. The critical role of the entrepreneur (which we will examine later) is not sufficiently allowed for, not to mention the roles of the people who identify market opportunities and who make the initial contact with real-life potential customers rather than abstractions in a plan.

Problems Looking for Solutions
vs. Solutions Looking for Problems

Technological innovation is most likely to be productive and viable over both the long and short term if a deliberate kind of continuing tension (one might call it "creative tension") is maintained between two different approaches to innovation. One involves challenging the R&D organization to discover the solution to perceived needs of the business, while the other results from the persistent, maybe even impassioned, advocacy of an inventor who sees an opportunity or latent need that he believes he can satisfy or who conceives a solution for which he seeks to demonstrate or even create a need.

The existence of this sort of creative tension or ritualized conflict has been noted in other aspects of scientific and technological endeavor,[25,31] in both the history of science and in the environment that makes for a more productive technical organization. A viable innovative function or organization must make it possible for a continuing conflict to occur between these two different approaches to the task. In order for ritualized conflict to be productive and viable, it is important for the respective roles of the various combatants to be generally recognized and for the rules and language of the struggle to be generally understood and followed. Otherwise, the conflict degenerates into a destructive brawl. One of the major objectives of this book is to clarify the roles of participants, to suggest the framework for struggle, and to formulate some of the language for the discourse.

One should not be misled by the reference to ritualism, however. The conflict takes skill and courage, and there are still clearly winners and losers. Careful examination of the Japanese culture is demonstrating the extended competitive struggle that may be masked under a cloak of pervasively ritualistic, carefully controlled behavior. It is incongruous to argue, as many have, that while the Japanese compete fiercely on the international front, the domestic scene is all cooperation and collusion. The Japanese would have to be remarkably schizophrenic to maintain such a dichotomy in their behavior. The value they place on achieving consensus and protecting face is well known. What is masked, until one becomes intimately familiar with the culture, is the elaborate and fiercely contested struggle that can be conducted by carefully ritualized means. And that is just the point—the Japanese culture is remarkably coherent and subtle, and yet it provides for internal strife. It carefully specifies culturally the rules of struggle in such a way that the "signals" of the opponents will not be misinterpreted. It provides rules for redress for those who have suffered unduly from compliance with consensus, it provides for dealing with pathological disturbances in which consensus is abrogated, and it also provides for discipline to reassert the continuing validity of the high value placed on consensus.

It is important to understand the significant features of these two approaches to innovation and the reason for needing conflict and competition between them. To be less dramatic, let us term the two types "demand-induced" innovation and "supply-pushed" innovation. That each has quite different characteristics is apparent from the widely differing descriptions one sees in case histories of innovation and in discussions of the innovation process (cf. Morton,[29] Schon,[33] and Meyers and Marquis[30]). The perceptions vary so widely that one wonders if these authors are describing the same process. Morton emphasizes the need for a systems view of innovation; yet it is apparent from his emphasis on science-based innovation and on the problems of pushing the innovation through to a successful conclusion that he is concerned principally with supply-pushed innovation.

Schon points out that the degree of disruption which invention creates is closely related to the resistance it will generate. His principal concern is with the high level of uncertainty associated with significant advances and with the managerial response to the uncertainty associated with such innovations. Meyers and Marquis exclude examination of "major innovations" from their study. They distinguish between demand recognition and feasibility recognition, and their survey indicates that only 21% of innovations studied were initiated by feasibility recognition.

Demand-Induced Innovation

Basically, demand-induced innovation receives its impetus from outside the R&D component itself. Somewhere in the rest of the organization a need is perceived and a demand is placed on the R&D component to devise a technical solution. Not surprisingly, these perceived needs will typically in some fashion make life easier for the requestor—they will lower cost, eliminate a nagging field problem, provide some kind of offset to a competitor's product, supply a request received from an important customer, or satisfy a perceived opportunity. This description excludes the special case (and it is a very large one) of the demand-induced innovation resulting from the procurement policies of the federal government in aerospace and defense. These policies have clearly stimulated and helped support the development of significant technological progress in many areas. They have not been characteristic of demand-induced innovation in the civilian sectors, however. Requests will tend to fall into two technical categories: those that represent incremental advances over present state-of-the-art and those that are essentially impossible, either because they defy nature or they involve constraints (usually economic) that nobody knows how to meet. The work needed to satisfy these requests has sometimes been termed micro-invention, and the label is apt, for most of these innovations have quite modest impact.

Demand-induced innovation has two other important characteristics. By comparison to the supply-pushed type, it is comparatively easy to bring to fruition. The need is already recognized, potential champions for the cause already exist, the risk of failure is frequently moderate to small, and the disruption to the organization is manageable. On the other hand, it is not easy to initiate in the R&D organization, since it originates on the outside.

So that this description will not be regarded as "damning by faint praise," let me hasten to add that this type of innovation is one of the most distinguishing characteristics of American industry, and it is tremendously important. Most of the innovation that occurs in the United States, defined not in terms of dollar value per innovation but rather in terms of numbers of changes successfully introduced, undoubtedly is of this type. And the

cumulative economic leverage is enormous. If we have any national characteristics that can themselves be regarded as industrial assets, the propensity
for seeking and incorporating continual improvement is surely one of them.
In all of the discussions during the 1960s about the technology gap and the
advantages the United States has supposedly enjoyed because of its effectiveness in generating and using technology, this crucial feature was largely
ignored. The glamour associated with space, with computers, and with
advanced electronics has tended to blind people to the much more prosaic,
tortoise-like elements in American technology. The unrelenting, almost
all-consuming, pursuit of cost reduction particularly but also of improvement in performance or features is perhaps *the* salient feature of American
management. The improvements frequently are small; technically they are
rarely pretentious; the achievements are usually anonymous even within
the organization; the advance in many cases is an elaboration or refinement
of an already mature technical field whose conceptual structure was worked
out long ago. Nevertheless, the cumulative progress that this work provides
represents the lifeblood of profitable operations. The assertion that "this
year's cost reductions are next year's profit margins" is frequently all too
true. If this phase relationship is not maintained, the business is in trouble.

One naturally asks: If this demand-induced innovative process accomp-
lishes so much and is fraught with so much less difficulty than the supply-
pushed type, why not stop right there? Why not establish an organization
that produces improvement on demand, and limit its charter and its aspirations to that kind of work? This pushbutton approach to creativity is
attractive because it offers the opportunity to finesse many of the disruptive
problems associated with supply-pushed innovation and the aggressive
innovators who bring it about. The only trouble is that an attempt to
impose such a limit fails to recognize some of the most salient and necessary
characteristics of creative people and of the organizations in which they
work. This approach says in effect (although admittedly somewhat exag-
gerated): "We want you creative people—individuals who won't be bound
by past methods, who will conceive of new approaches, who will cut
through all the clutter to find root problems—we want you to be nice docile
employees and create the solutions to the problems *we* pose. We'll point the
direction and establish the goals. You just get us there."

Obviously, such a policy is incompatible with the inherent nature of
people who are creative. Effective R&D organizations both resent and resist
pressure to conform to this role. It places the R&D group in the position of

being a servant to the rest of the organization. The fact that the work of the group may be greatly appreciated and generously rewarded is not adequate compensation for this subservient role. R&D people chafe at attempts to isolate them from other aspects of the business, which are made in a misguided belief that they are not interested in or should not have their creative energies diluted by such diversionary work or that they wouldn't be any good at it. They resent being told in effect that they have no business sense, that they cannot possibly perceive market needs or opportunities. Furthermore, a charter for innovative contribution which is limited to the role of fulfilling demand-induced innovation will severely constrict the creative capability that an R&D organization can attract and keep. As Anne Roe[32] demonstrated years ago, highly competent scientists have a strongly developed sense of autonomy. I think it can be safely said that most creative people share that characteristic. Consequently, they are not likely to be attracted to an organization if it seems to have little control over its own destiny.

Supply-Pushed Innovation

It is no doubt obvious that supply-pushed innovation is essentially opposite in character to that of demand-induced. It results from inventions and discoveries made in the R&D organization as a result of ideas generated from within, regardless of whether or not any need for the new capability has yet been expressed. Subsequent to the discovery, the R&D organization attempts to demonstrate the attractiveness of the opportunity thus created and to elicit support from operating management.

The forces that motivate work of this nature arise largely from the intrinsic nature of R&D and the characteristics of the technical people who work in R&D laboratories. The R&D organization builds up a body of expertise in selected areas, it establishes in programs a momentum that carries work along in terms of the internal logic inherent in the progress being made. These forces, together with the opportunities that creative technical people perceive for making high-leverage technical advances, drive the R&D organization to attempt to define its own destiny. Competent technical people feel very strongly that they are far better equipped to perceive and evaluate major technical opportunities than are other people—even other technical people; consequently, they strive for autonomy. It isn't surprising that people who have the intellectual and emotional capability to blaze new paths, to break with traditions, to throw out accepted concepts and tools, to risk failure from years of work are not particularly amenable to manipulation when it comes to accepting goals or objectives set by others.

Out of this supply-pushed type of innovation are most likely to appear the major achievements, the large discontinuities in technology. It is this type of innovation that Dr. Morton[29] tended to emphasize when he discussed innovation. It goes without saying that accomplishments of this magnitude are likely to be infrequent, that the risks of failure and the rewards for success will likely be high. Not surprisingly, the receptor organization tends to view opportunities of this magnitude very differently from those associated with demand-induced innovation. Many will see the high risk and large investment required and will respond with anxiety and caution. Others will see the disruption necessary to complete the process—the old techniques discarded, the expensive and painful learning required, the inherent hard work and disappointment along the path—and will respond with foot dragging and resistance. Others will see the changes in status, the downgrading of old skills, the necessary diversion of resources from their own pet projects or ideas, and will respond with resentment and counterattack. Still others will see the opportunity (both personal and business) and respond with enthusiasm. Thus, the receptor organization is likely to project a mixed array of attitudes and responses, which will represent far more of a barrier to the successful completion of the innovation than would be the case if it were demand-induced.

Major inventions of the supply-pushed type are relatively infrequent and have a relatively high failure rate. Consequently an organization chartered solely for work of this type has very dubious viability. The necessary level and breadth of support cannot be sustained in the receptor organization. On the other hand, its attractiveness to creative people is apparent. Such a charter emphasizes autonomy, it highlights the opportunity to pursue the big breakthrough, and it challenges the ambitious and feeds the ego. Thus, it creates the conditions that are more likely to attract and retain people who are highly competent and have driving motivation. The elimination of such inducements obviously will be done at a high price.

Fostering Creative Tension

Thus we come to the dilemma, the need for establishing and fostering two quite dissimilar, almost incompatible, kinds of innovation as objectives for R&D. An organization limited to demand-induced work finds it difficult to attract the talents requisite to success. Furthermore, demand-induced innovation in itself has been too limited in challenge to support a major commitment to innovation as a way to growth and success. The organization is saying in effect, "Don't try to change me any more than I want to be changed. Let me set the pace and the direction." Supply-pushed innovation, on the other hand, offers the opportunity to attract the talent necessary for highly creative R&D, and it sponsors the kind of effort that can produce the big advance which pays for many failures. However, no business will long tolerate or support an R&D organization with its expense, with its infrequent breakthroughs, and with its disruption and threat if it limits its objectives to the major accomplishments associated with supply-pushed innovation. Such an R&D component is likely to be regarded as an irresponsible alien. It would appear that a successful R&D organization must undertake both kinds of work simultaneously, that it must in fact foster a creative tension between the two in formulating its programs and allocating its resources.

There is an implicit assumption in much management thinking that successful management advances from the solution of one set of problems to the next set—presumably bigger and more challenging. In the management of innovation it begins to seem that successful management consists of living with problems—actually insuring that problems remain problems. "Permanent" solutions that resolve this "creative tension" for all time may be spelling the downfall of the organization.

Striving for Integrated Separation

Perhaps another way of saying it is that the manager of an R&D organization must strive for the incompatible goals of accomplishing integration and separation at the same time. Integration is necessary to achieve a sense of identification with the larger organization, to insure the inputs that provide the stimulation for demand-induced innovation, and to earn the opportunity to help define corporate purposes and objectives so that technical innovation can play its appropriate role in corporate strategy. Separation is needed to foster the autonomous outlook that will attract the free-thinking inventors and advocates who will conceive of, and fight through to, success on the major changes which give innovation its long-term viability and vitality.

In the era since World War II the emphasis has been on separation. Managers of fledgling R&D components have feared that they might be overrun or swallowed up by the parent organization and thus never acquire the capability, the self-respect, and the esteem of others needed to establish adequate influence for R&D. This view is understandable, probably even necessary, but it is also self-limiting. The organization component that persists in stressing its independence and its need for autonomy is, to others in the corporation, demonstrating its unwillingness to share the fortunes and the purposes of the total organization; it is alienating itself from the team. Such an organization may be tolerated because its accomplishments justify its existence, but it is limiting itself to playing a peripheral role.

There are some examples of R&D organizations that began from the opposite extreme, one of complete integration with, even servitude to, the rest of the organization—frequently in the guise of plant control labs. These components can come to occupy an important R&D role by dint of hard work and effectiveness, but they too encounter a barrier. The statuses and relationships established at an earlier period are difficult to change, and the R&D organization increasingly chafes at its junior status. It's hard to convince dad that you've grown up!

No matter which origin the R&D component has had, its long-run viability, the viability of the very concept of institutionalizing innovation, requires movement in the direction of establishing the creative tension described above. Such attempts to change roles and statuses are difficult and are even viewed with abhorrence by some. For the organization with an autonomous tradition, the change clearly brings new constraints. Many technical people will interpret it as diminishing their status and reducing their opportunities for personal achievement. For scientists, it will require a rebalancing of their loyalties between professional identification and their identification with the purposes and fortunes of a particular company. A compensating incentive, which initially may be only dimly perceived, is the fact that by accepting greater identification with the business and by seeking to insure that R&D does in fact make the optimum contribution, the R&D organization may be able to influence the formulation of company objectives and strategy and thereby achieve greater challenge for R&D than it has ever had before.

The task of moving from close integration toward more autonomy is harder for the R&D organization to accomplish on its own. Such a step requires at least the acquiescence if not the active support of the operating management, and that support may take a good deal of education to achieve. Since the principal consequence of the failure to do so is the likelihood of driving out key people who demand more autonomy and higher status than the situation permits, it may take the occurrence or near occurrence of such an event to provide the leverage for initiating the change. The loss of such people can border on the catastrophic. The manager of one highly technical business employing several thousand engineers once commented that the technical future of the business was really in the hands of six to ten key people.

Summary

The characterization of R&D which has been presented in this chapter does not lead to a warm feeling that permanent solutions *can* be devised for the problems that tug at our attention and energy. Ours is not an orderly world, but then our society and our own personal lives are full of inconsistencies and incompatibilities, which we somehow manage to live with. In fact, much of the spice and challenge of life is in developing the capability to live with these circumstances and to make of them the stuff of creative accomplishment.

If we are to succeed in turning the process of innovation into an institutionalized function, we had best come to understand the true nature of the animal. Success will require the ability to function effectively in a less structured and more tentative system; it will require an ability to accept the anxiety and ambiguity of uncertain solutions. Moreover, it will require the deliberate orchestration of ritualized conflict between protagonists for demand-induced innovation and supply-pushed innovation. We will have to identify the antagonists, specify the place and time of conflict, and generate the rules in order to determine winners and losers. This is not to suggest that an effective R&D organization should be a hotbed of hostility and recrimination. Ideally at least, the contest between protagonists should clarify not only objective data relevant to the opposing proposals but also the values and priorities of the participants. Thus, the contest should permit unity of purpose on chosen objectives, once they have been established. A major objective of this book is not only to argue for the need for "creative tension" but also to provide tools to help insure that the conflict is constructive.

3

The Corporate Environment
for Innovation

The meaning of the term "innovation" is not complex: introduction of new things or methods. Despite our regrettable tendency to debase words as we popularize their usage, I am not aware of any particular tendency to abuse this term by deviating from its traditional meaning. Its definition stresses the individual act, the act of bringing in something new. The emphasis is clearly on action, not on creation. However, the traditional meaning has been expanded to accommodate the word as the descriptor for a complex process, the process of creating and introducing new things or methods into common usage. Instead of focusing on the eventual result, the appearance of the new thing in usage, the term now implies what it takes to get it there, including the conception of the something new in the first place. In modern technical vernacular this could be interpreted as a systems view of innovation. Innovation is increasingly recognized as being a complex social process in which successful functioning requires the application of a diverse spectrum of skills, skills that almost miraculously might be found in a single individual or, failing that, could be collected within a group of people and coupled in the right sequence to keep the process going. I think it is also fair to say that principal attention is generally focused on innovation in products. The legitimacy of an innovation in process or procedure would be recognized, but most people think first of a new product when they think of innovation.

The process begins with the creator, the inventor who conceives something new; it moves to the perception of a use or the use to which something new can be put by society. The new thing must then be reduced to practice, i.e., it must be developed into something that really works to satisfy the perceived need and it must be producible by a reliable, economically feasible method. Finally, potential users must be identified and induced to purchase the product. Throughout this sequence somebody must be providing the resources and taking the risk. This individual, the entrepreneur, is the forcing function for the entire process, not only in providing the resources and in assuming the financial risk, but also in assuming the ego risk, the risk of failure, which is all too often overlooked.

The wonder is that innovation happens at all. It calls for a collection of talents whose confluence in a single individual can only be a statistical freak; even when sought in a collection of people, it requires skill and luck in assemblage. Furthermore, the entire process is fraught with anxiety, with the risk of failure, so that in addition to the necessary technical skills the people must have a belief and a commitment, a courage and a persistence that are invulnerable to the inevitable vicissitudes that accompany all innovations.

The R&D View of Innovation

While the meaning of the term "innovation" has gradually been undergoing a change, the meaning of the activity labeled R&D has also been broadened. Research and development refers to the process of generating new scientific knowledge and converting it into the technology that can be applied to practical affairs. It clearly focuses on the creative act, which is more or less in the background in the traditional definition of innovation. While research and development basically comprises the technical arm of innovation, it is coming to be confused with, or extended to include, the entire process.

Thus, in the minds and beliefs of many people, including the practitioners of technical work, the invention created through R&D is equated with innovation; or at least, the invention is regarded as being so dominant that all else is of little import. Seen through the eyes of the people dedicated to the creative task, it isn't surprising that they regard all other parts of the process as secondary to what they do. And I don't want in any way to depreciate its importance—clearly, without conception there won't be a baby. But the act of conception doesn't create an adult. When R&D people look down the road to innovation they see first their own kind, the inventors, as the stars of the show. Downstream from them and becoming increasingly smaller and fuzzier at successive stages are the development engineers who convert the invention into an economically and technically viable product; then the designers who prepare it for insertion into the industrial system by worrying about cost, about producibility, about specification of parts, materials, processes, etc.; and finally the manufacturing people who produce it as a salable unit. The existence of the salesman who locates and induces customers to buy this new, unproven product is perhaps recognized, but he is virtually invisible in the distance. In fairness it must be pointed out that the salesman's perspective is roughly the inverse of the inventor's. People in marketing are exceedingly conscious of the great effort required to develop a strategy for marketing a new product, to identify customers, to induce them to take a chance on an unproven product—in fact to discover the product's truly marketable virtues, since they frequently are not those first identified—and to develop pricing and distribution structures. Not surprisingly, the role of the inventor at the point of sale may appear dim and distant.

Innovation from Within vs. Starting Afresh

The process of innovation has two distinct operating modes, and while this discussion will focus on only one, the other must be mentioned. If one starts with the proposition that innovation is the process of creating and introducing change, then from the viewpoint of the total social system there are two options available. One can create or be fortunate enough to have a socioeconomic structure that fosters the creation of *new* organizations to accomplish each change. The other option is to create within existing organizations the capability to innovate, to introduce change, and thus modify themselves.

The first option finesses all or most of the problems of changing an existing organization. The "Route 128 complex" around Boston has come to be regarded as a model of a socioeconomic infrastructure that nurtured new organizations to accomplish innovation. In more general terms, and over a longer perspective, the entire American socioeconomic system is regarded as unusually well fitted for nurturing this kind of innovative activity, in comparison with more rigid, tradition-oriented societies. I have nothing but admiration for the success stories the choosers of this option generate, and I recognize the vital role they play in maintaining the long-run viability of our total system. I am convinced, however, that in a world growing ever more crowded and dominated by giant organizations and giant institutions in all spheres of life, it is far more crucial to understand and, if possible, improve on the effectiveness of the process of innovation in large organizations. We must continue to encourage and reward the individual inventor-entrepreneur, but we dare not ignore the much more difficult problem of maintaining the viability of the very large corporation, a viability that is fostered by achieving skill in innovation.

The Role of the Entrepreneur

Let us assume the invention has been made. I know that this step is paramount and that the care and feeding of the creative R&D people who make it is an important problem, but it is the total process of innovation about which we must become more knowledgeable. The next crucial ingredient the sponsoring organization must supply is the entrepreneur, and he may or may not be the same individual as the inventor. In fact, one reason for believing that innovation in the large organization is so terribly important is that such organizations at least provide the possibility of combining in a group of people, structured in a suitable way, the diverse talents needed for innovation, which nature so rarely bestows on a single individual. The entrepreneur, the advocate and risk taker, is indispensable in a large organization as well. Furthermore, his commitment must be total, just as it is if he is trying to innovate by creating a new enterprise.

Innovation is not a part-time task. The problems and obstacles are too obstinate to yield to only occasional attention. Furthermore, the skills and point of view required in an entrepreneur are in many respects antithetical with those required for success in other kinds of business. In those areas where stewardship is the paramount value, the emphasis will be placed on maintaining balance, on weighing alternatives, on keeping perspective. In contrast, the single-mindeness, the bias, and the unrelenting persistence of the entrepreneur can seem wrong, almost irrational to those not so committed.

Why should anyone make such a commitment, accept such punishment to his ego, run such a risk? The common belief is that the entrepreneur is motivated by the opportunity he perceives for large rewards, financial or otherwise, which make the goal worth striving for. The proposition that large opportunities for reward provide incentive for undertaking large risks raises the question of how a large organization can respond adequately. How can it provide rewards commensurate with the risks? The autonomous entrepreneur creating a new enterprise is "going for broke"; if the mission fails, the organization will disappear; if it succeeds, he will reap all the rewards or at least will himself allocate the rewards. It is virtually impossible for a large company to offer equivalent opportunity. Why should the entrepreneur work within the framework of a large organization? The three parameters that can be manipulated in attempting to provide adequate incentive are risk, reward, and effort; and, as we will see, the large organization is not hopelessly outclassed.

Managing Entrepreneurial Risk

Risk must be considered in three parts: *intrinsic risk*, i.e., what is the probability that the venture will succeed or fail; *personal financial risk*, i.e., to what extent are the individual's personal financial resources and future earning capacity at stake; and *ego risk*, i.e., what impact will failure have on the individual himself? Intrinsic risk is more or less in the lap of the gods and in the inherent capabilities of the entrepreneur, irrespective of the organizational context in which he is working. Thus, the large corporation suffers no disadvantage.

The situation for personal risk is quite different. The autonomous entrepreneur is typically risking all or most of his personal assets and even his future capacity to earn. Thus, if he fails, the damage to him and his family is enormous. The corporate entrepreneur faces no such problem. His own money is not committed nor is his future earning power likely to be as severely disrupted. In this area the large organization has an enormous advantage to exploit. In particular this advantage broadens the population of otherwise qualified potential entrepreneurs who cannot or would not run the necessary personal financial risk. Since the necessary talents are always rare, anything that enlarges the list of potential candidates is a valuable advantage.

On the other hand, with respect to ego risk, each situation has distinctive features that may appeal to different people. The autonomous entrepreneur is working in a nonhierarchical world. True, he may even plead for money, but when he does he is talking to a man whose future connection with the activity will only be financial, not one who is his "superior" in the organization. He is not caught up in an overlying network of statuses and relationships in a larger formal organization. If the individual entrepreneur fails, he will tend to perceive it as his own inadequacy or the workings of fate in an unstructured world. He will not be able to focus blame on an organization whose systematic structure and visibility invites attack. For some, this situation is undoubtedly preferable.

The change in perspective can be dramatic. An associate once commented on the remarkable change in attitude of a fledgling firm recently spun off from a major corporation. The managers were at great personal risk. All realized that each month could be their last and that the margin for error or accident was nonexistent. Nevertheless, they felt that the problem was *all* theirs and that they were confronting it *directly* rather than through the filter of a larger management structure. Consequently, an exhilarating dedication pervaded the organization.

In contrast, if the corporate entrepreneur fails, he can blame his manager, an organization ill-equipped to sponsor innovation, organizational rivals who refused to cooperate—a host of convenient and perhaps even legitimate targets. This opportunity to diffuse the blame may be more appealing to some.

However, for the corporate entrepreneur, the specific consequences of failure are largely beyond his control. The autonomous entrepreneur will pick up the pieces as best he can, find a job somewhere, move back in with the in-laws—whatever can be done to start life over again. The corporate entrepreneur will to a considerable extent have his fate decided for him; he may be fired, transferred, demoted, possibly even promoted. Thus, there is substantial opportunity to focus and personalize resentment, and also opportunity for other potential entrepreneurs to pass judgment on the fate meted out to the unsuccessful ones in a large organization.

Perhaps most important is that corporate management has the opportunity to influence the way in which ego risk will be perceived. If the large organization truly wishes to nurture entrepreneurship, it must approach the subject of risk with great sensitivity and with a keen regard for the equities of all the participants. Decisions on personal commitment are basically made on a subjective appraisal of the balance of risk and reward, and if the penalties for failure are regarded as too high, the commitment will never be made. The organization unhappy with the extent to which risk taking is assumed would do well to reexamine its equation of risk, penalty, and reward.

The relative attractiveness of corporate versus autonomous entrepreneurship with respect to ego risk appears to be a standoff. Each has advantages which can appear attractive to some. The large corporation has the advantage—if it is perceptive enough and wishes to do so—of mitigating the ego risk associated with the disappointing entrepreneurial thrusts.

Managing Reward

The area of reward also offers special advantages for each entrepreneurial framework. The autonomous entrepreneur has a clear advantage in financial reward. Large corporations cannot compete effectively with the financial gains available to even the moderately successful entrepreneur, much less the dramatic successes that earn headlines. The president of a large company may retire as a multimillionaire, but he won't have become one by the time he is 35, or probably even 50.

In other areas of reward which have to do principally with ego gratification, the relative advantages are less certain. For those who place great value on being their own boss and on creating their own personal monument, the corporate route has little attraction. Conversely, the task of maintaining the long-term viability of large enterprise is quite different from that of starting one successfully, which in turn differs from the challenge of growing an enterprise into regional or even national prominence. If a man aspires to expanding power and influence, to the positions that manipulate larger and larger events, the large organization at least has an opportunity to provide attractive incentive. It all depends on what it does with its successful entrepreneurs and its successful enterprises. If it encourages its entrepreneurs, but promotes its stewards or its politicians to the senior positions, it may find its hopes for entrepreneurial growth disappointed. If somehow, by word and deed, it says "entrepreneurs are crucial to our future—we want them—we will reward them financially as much as we can—we expect much of our senior management to come from them," it is much more likely to be successful in attracting people with entrepreneurial ambitions and in eliciting the personal commitment necessary for success in entrepreneurial endeavor.

Managing Effort

In the situation with respect to effort, the large organization has a distinct advantage. Life for the autonomous entrepreneur can be a maddening round of scrambling desperately for resources, of seeing progress severely impeded, and success even denied by the inadequacy of resources. While the corporation indeed does have limited resources, once it has made the commitment of support it can relieve the entrepreneur of the task of fighting even for shoestring support, and can instead enable him to concentrate on the work of exploiting the opportunity. But by the same token, the too-ready provision of resources may encourage the formulation of too grandiose or too ambitious plans. The fledgling business must sooner or later face the stern test of producing profits, and overly generous support not only lengthens the period of uncertainty but also increases the investment burden that the business must eventually support.

The opposite danger is probably even more likely—that an anxious top management will stare the fledgling business to death. A common reason for bootlegging embryonic innovations is to avoid the spotlight of corporate attention and the concomitant endless round of reviews and presentations requested by corporate management.

Summary

From the foregoing discussion it can be seen that advantages and disadvantages accrue to both the autonomous entrepreneur and the corporate entrepreneur. The advantages of personal financial gain clearly lie with the autonomous approach, balanced by higher personal financial risk. The large corporation can offer avenues to positions of high status and power if it demonstrates that entrepreneurial success is one of the best routes to the top. It can also reduce the frustrating diversion of effort needed to persuade sponsors to provide support. That there are powerful reasons for the large corporation to seek to encourage entrepreneurial behavior will be shown in later discussion. It is important to recognize that not all the cards are stacked against it in the competition for entrepreneurial talent.

Thus far we have been considering the relative potential advantages and disadvantages of a large corporation in fostering innovation, compared to those of an autonomous entrepreneur. Whether or not a large business will succeed in capitalizing on its potential advantages will depend on whether the entire organization is well enough structured to initiate and nurture innovation. In Chapter 4 we will examine the relationship between organization and innovation, and in Chapter 5 we will consider the management climate for innovation.

4   Organizing for Innovation

When innovation is attempted within the confines of an ongoing organization, it is apparent that an adequate understanding of the process requires examination of the context in which it occurs. The relationship of innovation with, and its impact on, contiguous activities, functions, and other organizational components are crucial to its success, and understanding the nature of these relationships is mandatory to understanding the nature of innovation itself.

The commitment to innovation can easily become a monster, not only devouring the limited financial resources of the organization, but also draining the emotional and physical resources of the management and creating discord and recrimination within the entire organization. When one takes into account the inherently disruptive, chaos-creating element in innovation, is it not naive and illogical to consider ways to keep it under control, to make it responsive to guidance and direction? It would be just as naive to assume that large organizations do not already have substantial conflict in the competition of functional components for power and resources and in the struggle at the top of the organization to establish corporate goals and plans. The decisions on resource allocation, corporate goals, and corporate strategy require the evaluation of complex and intangible subjects that will not be adequately explored unless capable, strong-minded men confront each other as proponents for different points of view. Thus, some of the problems inherent in institutionalizing innovation are not exactly strangers to corporate management.

One of the crucial aspects of the institutionalization of change is the character of organization needed to foster change. Much effort has gone into examination of organizations from the standpoint of achieving operational efficiency, but little attention has been paid to the general problem of the efficiency of the organization in generating, accepting, and implementing change. It seems clear that if we are to succeed in our effort to institutionalize the generation of change, we must consider the organizational framework in which this activity can function most effectively. Since by definition the generation of change constitutes a disruptive, intrusive activity, it is clear that there is a crucial relationship between the organization that is responsible for producing change (say, the R&D organization) and the associated organization that will be the receptor of the change and which must provide continuing sponsorship for its creation. Hence, in considering the organization of change, we must perforce look first outside the R&D organization. We will leave the question of the organization of the R&D function itself to Chapter 10.

Structure vs. Dynamics

Organization studies typically are concerned with two general classes of questions. One involves essentially matters of structure—one could call it "anatomy." The other involves matters of dynamics having to do primarily with the allocation and control of power. It is almost impossible to think of organization without beginning with the orderliness or systematization that the term "structure" connotes. Certain esthetic standards are applied in examining an organization structure. It is assumed that an effective organization will have a character of neatness, of internal coherence, which arises from a number of features. The first is a general conceptual framework that provides a way of thinking about doing the work of the business. For example, what will be the basic building blocks? One can discover successful enterprises structured around a variety of unifying principles such as geography, products, markets, and technology. The effort to articulate the basic structural framework will focus on establishing clarity and completeness to insure that all the work which has to be done is identified, characterized, and assigned to some position. A related question involves the hierarchical distribution of authority and responsibility. Will the authority pyramid be tall with many layers, or flat with few layers? This facet of organization structuring basically involves careful delineation of functional responsibilities, of the relationships and couplings between functions, and of the hierarchical relationships that will channel authority, responsibility, and communication. Those who see organization principally as structure will regard the task as finished when these basic blocks of work have been completed.

The dynamic aspects of organization planning recognize that the functioning of an organization is essentially a political process because it involves the cooperative and frequently the competitive behavior of people. If the organization is to be effective in achieving its objectives, courses of action must be chosen—sometimes among alternatives and sometimes among competing courses of action—and then it must be possible to command the resources necessary to accomplish chosen objectives, once they are established. The work involved in choosing courses of action and in commanding resources is essentially an exercise of power. Effective organization planning must make provision for the proper allocation of power and for proper control of the exercise of power.

Two particular features must be considered in examining an organization in this dynamic sense. The first is, what means are provided for the resolution of conflict? The second involves the management of risk. It is inevitable, when choices must be made and when capable ambitious people coexist in an organization, that strong conflicts of interest will emerge and that difficult choices will have to be made. The organization must provide for a structure in which review at some higher level creates: (1) responsibility for and (2) power to make a choice between competing functions or competing points of views and then to marshal resources to move in the chosen direction. By the same token the effective control—one might almost call it the management of power—requires consideration of the allocation of power so as to maintain viability and to protect minority interests in much the same way that our country's founders gave careful thought to checks and balances in the development of the structure of our federal government.

In managerial discussions devoted to reorganization proposals, concern over alterations in the balance of power is clearly evident. Managers will not willingly create formidable competition for themselves. Even in designing specific positions, attention is given to the question of whether too much power is being placed in one position without adequate checks by other parts of the structure. On occasion the desire to avoid creation of too powerful a position may even lead to curtailment of authority to the extent that it impairs the ability of any incumbent to perform effectively. Interestingly enough, explicit consideration of the adequacy of "checks and balances" (and those are the terms used) is a factor in executive deliberations regarding organization.

On the other hand, when we begin to consider organization planning from the standpoint of insuring effectiveness in sponsoring and implementing change, of creating innovation, we must adopt a different set of perspectives. Fundamentally, innovation involves a risk-taking prospect. Thus, the second crucial question in examining organizational dynamics is: "How can we divide up risk into manageable proportions so that individuals will be able to deal with it, will be able to live with the anxiety that it inevitably creates?" We must also ask: "How can we be sure that the risk evaluations and the decisions to take risk—which should be made if the business is to remain viable and be successful in introducing innovation—do in fact get made?" It is true that some things get accomplished simply by inaction or the failure to make decisions, but innovation is not one of them. It requires aggressive, forceful action to face up to a risky innovation opportunity, to evaluate it, and to make a decision to incur the risk.

Managing Risk

If one is to introduce the management of risk as an explicit element to be taken into account in organization planning, it is necessary to give explicit consideration to two parameters, which are usually ignored in such planning. These parameters are the element of time and the element of probability. The element of time is so important to understanding the institutionalization of change that we must make a substantial exploration of this topic before considering the element of probability. One frequently hears references to time as an element of business decision making and of the necessity to balance long range and short range as a major element in management. In fact, the management of time and the problems created by the difficulties inherent in making time trade-offs are rarely explicitly taken into account in developing an organization structure and in assigning responsibilities to specific positions. Taking account of the element of time means first the development of an explicit and systematic time profile of the evaluations and decisions required in order to provide for both the short-range and the long-range needs of the business. Then specific responsibility must be assigned across the entire spectrum of the time profile in such a way as to insure effective advocacy for all parts of the time spectrum and for sound trade-offs among various parts of the spectrum.

"Taking account" of the element of time requires a series of specific steps. First, one must establish the time frame within which management attempts to operate—whether it be 2 or 20 years—and then one must develop a systematic time profile of the plans, evaluations, and decisions that are required to provide for the business within this time frame. The second step—assigning responsibility for all the necessary work, including all segments of the time profile—is childishly obvious, except that it contains hidden pitfalls. Businessmen are well aware that in examining investment trade-offs, they must discount the future, that the present and near-term future is worth more than the more distant future. A moment's reflection indicates that the same process applies to the allocation of their own time and energy; present problems are worth more attention than future problems. Thus, in assigning responsibility in terms of time, care must be exercised to insure that the distribution of responsibility is such that concern over the present does not always drive out concern over the future—a perennial problem.

The typical organizational arrangement is to assign responsibility in such a way that each manager is supposed to "balance long-run and short-run considerations". Under these circumstances it should be no surprise to hear the almost universal complaint that short-run profit considerations are being weighted to the virtual exclusion of all else. Since discounting the future is inevitable, only the specific assignment of explicit and primary responsibility for the future (to the virtual exclusion of the present) to managers of force and high status will insure that the future gets the attention it requires. Note that this assignment cuts across functional lines. It also differs from the responsibility for the daily operation of a business.

If time is to be adequately taken into account, three different kinds of activity must be recognized and allowed for: the planning and operating work associated with the ongoing life of the business; the planning and evaluating associated with the future (including the introduction of change); and the balancing and decision making required to maintain a viable equilibrium between the two. Even more important is the need to recognize that responsibility for these three kinds of work must be kept separate if they are to be performed adequately; otherwise the present will always drive out the future.

Institutionalizing the introduction of change requires the deliberate fostering of a creative tension between those charged with stewardship of the present business and those charged with maintaining its long-term viability, including the generation of change. The mediating role of making trade-offs between the two protagonists has to be reserved to yet a third party. Perhaps most important is that each actor in this play must have the muscle to be an effective protagonist for his position; otherwise the "creative tension" never exists.

In the interests of fairness I should note that all the good planning and balancing in the world comes to naught if execution is faulty. Nevertheless, I do not intend to consider the latter because it has already received generous attention. I am more concerned with the persistence of the "short-term considerations dominate corporate action" syndrome and with stressing the need for assigning explicit responsibility for "making the case for the future" to powerful, high-status executives.

The Role of the Large Corporation

The kind of role specialization (implicit in what we have been saying) makes sense only for the very large corporation, which is the particular focus of this book. A series of trends is converging to require this level of specialization. Large corporations represent such extensive aggregations of capital, of human talent, and of productive capacity that their long-term viability is a matter of national interest. If management devotes inadequate attention to maintaining this long-term viability, it will inevitably find its sphere circumscribed by governmental intervention. Developing the capacity to initiate and/or respond to change is an inescapable component of viability. Thus, the institutionalization of change is a natural adjunct to the growing time perspective of the giant company.

Fortunately, the appearance of this need to adopt a long time horizon is occurring as our technological capability and our knowledge base are expanding to enable us to develop tools appropriate to the task. The development of sophisticated modeling techniques, of computers to exercise the models, and of extensive data bases to furnish the needed inputs now make it possible to plan, project, and explore alternatives in a time frame that would have been futile only a few years ago. In order for these tools to be used effectively, it is necessary not only to employ people with the necessary skills, but also to develop a role structure that places them in a status sufficiently high so that their inputs will indeed be heard and given due weight by those responsible for formulating strategy. The deliberate introduction of a time horizon as an element of organization structuring is needed to establish this role specialization. Attempts to assign responsibility for making the case for different time frames to the same individual will not suffice—the present drives out the future. Furthermore, people will not have the time or incentive to become adequately specialized in the possible scenarios associated with different time horizons.

Assignment of responsibility along a common time frame provides a powerful unifying influence for management action and especially for management communication. Technical people in R&D often discover with surprise that they share a greater community of interest with nontechnical people in product planning whose responsibilities match the time frame of R&D than they do with technical people struggling with short-term problems. It is exceedingly difficult to get the attention of an engineer whose project is behind schedule or whose principal supplier has just gone on strike. Conversely, a marketing man trying to fathom what products the business should be selling in five years will typically be quite receptive to discussions with people in R&D.

Stewardship vs. Agent of Change

The division of responsibility according to a common time frame makes it possible to create another type of unifying role specialization as well—the separation of the stewardship role from that of being an agent of change charged with maintaining the long-term viability of the business. At the general manager level this distinction is perhaps best elucidated by differentiating between profit responsibility and entrepreneurial responsibility. The general manager who is permitted to focus on profit responsibility can emphasize the stewardship role with respect to the resources of the business. In fulfilling this role he focuses on making trade-off decisions among the various functions that make up the business, seeking to optimize profits in a relatively undifferentiated time frame. In contrast, the general manager charged with entrepreneurial responsibility focuses on "whole business" trade-offs—leaving functional trade-offs to others—and of necessity balances long term versus short term in his management of resources.

Just as the present drives out the future when responsibility for the two is combined in one man, the responsibility for functional trade-offs tends to drive out entrepreneurial trade-offs when the two are combined. The point of view required in the two cases is quite different. In one the manager is asking how much he should spend on engineering versus manufacturing versus marketing, and toward what objectives; in the other he is analyzing the relative attractiveness of one business opportunity versus another, assuming both will be executed optimally. Here he must take account explicitly of the time frame of judging payoffs in the business alternatives. When the two responsibilities are combined, the general manager finds that the demands of his responsibilities for generating profits dominate his own available time and energy. He may or may not be censured for being ineffective in carrying out his entrepreneurial responsibility, but he will certainly be censured (probably fired) for failing to generate profits, which in the short run depend on managing and integrating the functional activities effectively.

This tendency in measurement to emphasize short-run profits is amplified by a common managerial assumption relative to the significance of present profitability as a measure of the attractiveness of an opportunity. As one executive said about a business reporting to him, which was alleged to have great growth potential, "Those people have to discipline themselves to demonstrate that they can operate profitably. Then I will give them the money to grow." In a society in which investment opportunities are evaluated by their ability to generate profits and in which there is great uncertainty in projecting future profitability, it is not surprising that general managers who have seen many rosy predictions turn sour will demand profits as the proof of the attractiveness of the opportunity. Hence, the general manager with combined profit and entrepreneurial responsibility very sensibly and frequently decides to focus his attention on profits and neglects entrepreneurial endeavors that might jeopardize short-term profitability.

This decision, interestingly enough, is often relatively insensitive to the current profit status of the business. As one would expect during periods of poor profit performance, there are overwhelming pressures to focus all resources on reducing costs and reestablishing profitable operation. Conversely, during periods of rapid growth there are strong pressures to devote all available manpower and managerial energy to capitalizing on the immediate opportunity so as not to lose market position. Thus, even though the business has large sums available to invest in future-oriented work, it frequently is unable to divert the manpower to undertake it during times of great success.

For the large, multibusiness corporation, the pattern of organization that

will facilitate the institutionalization of change now begins to emerge.
Within the individual business component, work is organized according to
functional specialties, with people operating in a relatively undifferentiated
near-term time frame and with the general manager optimizing
profitability. At the multibusiness level, people are organized according to a
common long-term time frame rather than according to functional specialization, charged with making an effective case for the future—including the
generation of change to maintain the long-term viability of the business(es).
The general manager at this level makes whole business trade-offs,
mediating between his protagonists for the future (i.e., the agents of
change) and his protagonists for the present (i.e., the stewards of the
present businesses).

This description is obviously idealized and real-world situations will
rarely correspond to the model. In fact, all general managers, including
those who have little or no entrepreneurial responsibility, undoubtedly do
give some consideration to the long term. Plant capacity must be added as
needed, long-term adequacy of labor supply must be insured, etc. Furthermore, "long term" means very different things in different businesses.
In the extractive industries and in heavy capital equipment, time perspective must exceed a decade, whereas in housewares it will be much shorter.
Nevertheless, it is important to recognize the powerful and consistent bias
in favor of the short run, which is operative when responsibility for long-
and short-run considerations is combined. As one would expect, some rare
managers are indeed able to balance long and short terms and give adequate
consideration to both profit and entrepreneurial responsibility. But the
successful institutionalization of change requires an organizational structure that will permit adequate attention to the future with the typical
managerial talent available; it cannot rely on the rare individual who can
swim against the tide of relentless pressure to achieve short-term profit
growth. Thus, recognition of the need to separate responsibility for making
the case for the future from operating in the present, and to foster a
deliberate tension between the two, which in turn is resolved at a higher
level, is an important step in the successful institutionalization of change.

Implications for R&D

The implications of this point of view for R&D are very important. R&D
is inherently a futures-oriented organization. If it is the only such futures

MILLS COLLEGE
LIBRARY

component in a business otherwise organized to focus on stewardship, R&D will face an exceedingly difficult task in even getting the attention of others, much less obtaining effective commitment to introduce change. The successful introduction of change involves multifunctional participation and accommodation, and unless futures-oriented people exist in the other functions, the process will be seriously impeded.

The distorted view of innovation noted earlier, which emphasizes the R&D contribution to innovation, has perhaps helped impede the growth of futures-oriented people dedicated to change in the other functions. Analysis of the performance of many R&D organizations indicates that those most successful in actually helping to introduce innovation interact broadly throughout an organization. They help not only engineering in the development and design of new product; they also help manufacturing learn how to manufacture new products and operate new processes; and they also work closely with marketing in identifying and evaluating new market and product opportunities. Where these relationships do not exist—or, more importantly, where there are no people in the other functions charged, as in R&D, with trying to generate change—the R&D component faces a frustrating and uncertain future.

One could argue that as the institutionalization of change matures, the need will be recognized for a new function, innovation, which includes representatives from all other functions, which operates within a common time frame for future action, and which will supersede R&D. Whether this role specialization will work best by being pulled together into a single new functional component to create a powerful "case for the future" or diffused as an explicit subfunction throughout all functions is not yet clear. What *is* clear is the need to insure that people whose responsibilities give them matching time horizons (an engineer would call it an impedance match) is indispensable to achieve commercialization of R&D outputs.

Management of Risk

We are now able to relate the problem of the management of risk in a large company to the situation facing an autonomous entrepreneur, as discussed in Chapter 3, and to show how a large company can improve its attractiveness with respect to individual risk taking.

An important added benefit that this approach to organization achieves is to divide up risk into more manageable quantities. On the one hand, people who must make risky decisions involving functional trade-offs can at least limit themselves to that kind of activity without at the same time complicating life by making time trade-offs. On the other hand, people charged with making the case for the future do not have to make near-term functional trade-offs. Finally, the general manager charged with entrepreneurial balancing of near term and long range knows that dedicated efforts have gone into making the case for each.

The division of risk into individually manageable portions requires explicit consideration in organization planning; otherwise, people will persistently mortgage the future in order to reduce near-term risk. Each of us has a saturation level of the risk he can tolerate, beyond which the risk is sublimated in some fashion. Since people rarely get fired for depreciating the attention devoted to the future, the safest course for the individual so saturated is simply to ignore the long term. The normal dynamics of managerial movement also contribute to this short-term perspective. It is a truism that the most important reward for good performance is a promotion to a better job and not just a good raise in salary. Therefore, a management system that leads to short average times in a position encourages a manager to adopt a short-time perspective because he will not be around long enough to get either the credit or the blame for future-oriented activity.

The need to reduce risk to manageable proportions must also be addressed from the standpoint of the size of the risk compared with the profit base that will be supporting the venture. Obviously, the smaller the ratio of risk to profit base, the less the personal threat to the man incurring the risk and the greater the probability that he will decide to undertake the venture. As we will see in Chapter 5, our industrial system is becoming less and less forgiving of failure to achieve profit objectives. Unfortunately, the mere fact that nature didn't cooperate or that exceedingly difficult cost estimates turned out to be wrong is not truly accepted as an excuse. The manager supporting a venture whose investment requirements seriously affect profits will be under the most extreme pressure to correct the situation, irrespective of the long-term value of the venture.

For some rare individuals this possibility will be no deterrent—they can stand the heat. And, indeed, one might say that high risks *should* be incurred in order to reap the high rewards that are possible under our economic system. As we found earlier, however, these large rewards tend to be associated primarily with the autonomous entrepreneur because the large corporation is handicapped in seeking to provide commensurate rewards.

Consequently, it must take care to avoid a risk/reward ratio that deters rather than stimulates the undertaking of risks. Furthermore, the institutionalization of change will not succeed if it depends on the participation of exceedingly rare people. A large corporation must design its entrepreneurial structure in such a way as to keep risk at tolerable levels.

Recognition of the distinction between profit responsibility and entrepreneurial responsibility, with the latter being withheld to higher organizational levels, is responsive to this requirement. Since the total decision structure now encompasses a multibusiness base, the "bets" on the future can now become more numerous, and probabilities that at least some will be successful now begin to become more favorable. A single business unit has little choice except to "go for broke" on one venture or to pass up the opportunity altogether. Even then, however, some entrepreneurial opportunities are so large that they generate an unacceptable risk for the responsible manager. Unless a way can be found to move the risk to a larger profit base (i.e., higher in the corporate structure), such opportunities will not be exploited,[37] or the opportunity will be redefined more narrowly so as to reduce the risk, even though it results in a significantly lower long-run profit potential. The Sappho[37] studies at the University of Sussex have demonstrated the importance of a high-level corporate sponsor in successful innovation.

This emphasis on reducing risk to manageable proportions may seem to imply that managers of large corporations are timid souls who have no business pretending to be potential entrepreneurs. While some undoubtedly fit that description, it is grossly unfair to many. The institutionalization of change requires that entrepreneurial behavior become a way of life. The inevitable conflict between change and stewardship must be so orchestrated that both will have powerful advocates. Since the autonomous entrepreneur initially has little or no stewardship responsibility, analogies based on his experience must be treated carefully. The enormous, relentless pressure for profitable performance which managers of large businesses absorb means that efforts to insert still more risk into the environment must be carefully tuned to the circumstances if they are to succeed. The role specialization discussed in this chapter is a step in this direction.

Summary

We have been examining the way in which the organization structure of the total corporation can foster or impede innovation. Two factors are especially important: insuring that time is properly factored into decision making and that risk is divided up in such a way that it will be accepted rather than avoided as a rational element of profit seeking.

Since men tend to discount the future even in their own behavior, it is necessary to assign explicit and undiluted responsibility for the far term at some level in the organization if the future is ever to receive the effective advocacy it must have for innovation to flourish. This requirement cuts across all functions and if such an assignment does not occur, R&D as a futures-oriented function will find it difficult to couple with the rest of the organization. Matching of time horizons is necessary for technology to move along the spectrum to application.

At the same time, risk taking must be related to the size of the business base. Since a large corporation cannot reward risk takers comparably with the potential financial return for autonomous entrepreneurs, it must be certain that its risk/reward ratio does not deter innovative risk taking. Two ways to manage risk effectively are to assign responsibility high enough so that the risk is small compared with the business base, or to initiate a sufficient number of ventures to permit the actuarial probabilities of success to be more attractive.

5

The Climate for Innovation in Corporate Management

Most of the research on, and discussion of, R&D management has focused on the internal aspects of managing an R&D organization, looking at such matters as project selection, technical communication, and recruiting and rewarding creative technical people. One cannot deny the importance of topics such as these; however, a systems appraisal must also consider the interface between as well as the inputs to and from R&D and the rest of the corporation. In particular, the nature of the management climate in operations is of crucial importance. After all, it is this management group that must provide support for the R&D organization, must concur in the technical and business objectives it chooses, and must accept R&D outputs for incorporation into the mainstream of operations. In listening to managers of R&D talk about the matters that concern them most, it is clear that dealing with operating management constitutes one of their major challenges. In fact, except at lower levels of R&D management, more managerial time and effort probably go into contending with problems involving the interface with operating management than with internal affairs of the R&D operation.

What sort of problem does operating management pose? How much does it understand of what R&D can provide and how it should be related to the rest of the business? What hang-ups does it have that will complicate interaction? What pressures does it face that will impede the effective functioning of R&D? These and similar questions are as important to achieving effective performance in R&D as are the questions addressing internal matters.

Pressures on Operating Management

The cult of performance looms as the key factor in understanding the response of American management to the trend toward institutionalizing change. The investing public expects a company to become a machine for generating profits and growth. Management is subjected to continuing coercive comparison to the achievement of other companies, not only companies whose products provide direct competition, but also companies of whatever character that represent alternative investment opportunities. The relationship between this competitive comparison and the efficient use and allocation of capital is readily apparent, and its economic consequences are accepted as desirable. Just as important, however, is the psychological imperative this comparison creates as a measure of managerial competence.

Furthermore, the system has become very unforgiving of disappointing performance. The mere fact that profits and/or growth did not meet expectations, even though by objective standards they might have represented excellent performance under the circumstances, is enough to subject management to criticism. Consequently, corporate executives are forced into an inexorable quest for improvement in earnings. Product differentiation, cost reduction, improved product performance, and penetration of new markets are perennial goals whose formulation and attainment demand a significant fraction of managerial resources.

One might conclude that such an environment is ideally receptive to R&D, which, after all, represents one of the most attractive avenues available for achieving the improved performance management seeks. While this conclusion is undoubtedly valid, it must be balanced against countervailing influences, the most important of which is management's parallel quest for certainty. To a very considerable extent, American operating management is in the business of creating certainty, partly as a personal imperative and partly in response to an unforgiving investment public. Despite all the talk about taking risks and the recognition that R&D is a game of probabilities, failures are unfortunately still regarded as failures in the business community, and no matter what disclaimers are given, they don't advance one's career as even a modest success would do. Operating managers devote enormous time and energy to identifying the risks and uncertainties inherent in contemplated courses of action, and to defining targets in such a way as to maximize the likelihood of achieving them. The investment community doesn't like surprises, and failure to achieve expected results shakes the confidence of investors in the validity of their appraisal of management's competence. In business operations a continual bias operates in the direction of preferring a smaller more certain goal over a larger more risky one. It goes without saying that this bias has a particularly antithetical effect on creative scientists and engineers who are seeking to create supply-pushed innovations.

This preference for smaller risks is being reinforced by the increasing sophistication and the tighter control being achieved in planning and in measuring performance in business operations. The internal looseness that might absorb and obscure mistakes in planning or in the risky ventures that did not succeed is being squeezed out. There are few places to hide uncertainty in a system subjected to ever tighter and more searching control. This environment can constitute a pretty unfriendly context for the proponent of R&D ventures with the risks that are inherent in them. The operating manager has quite valid reasons for the discomfort or reluctance he may display when asked to support an R&D venture.

Managerial Style

Another critical area to explore in examining the management climate for R&D is the subject of management style, particularly as it affects the formulation of business strategy. Much attention is being given today to the development of conceptual tools and analytical techniques for improving the rationality of management planning and decision making. Nevertheless, after all the information has been gathered and all the sophisticated analysis is completed, crucial choices will still have to be made regarding goals to be sought, means to be adopted, and rates of change to be attempted. Nowhere does the general manager project his own values, his own judgment, his own life style as much as in formulating the basic purposes and strategy of the business.

Despite an unending quest for rigorous analytical techniques that will reveal the optimum, one must recognize that a truly adequate analysis of a business situation must include the characteristics of the decision maker himself. There is no uniquely optimum strategy that can leave out the knowledge, experience, judgment, and *will* of the managers who will be making the decisions and, even more, who will be accepting the risk. A manager is most likely to be successful in pursuing goals and strategies when he feels most capable of implementing them effectively. He will tend to make decisions along directions with which he feels most comfortable. Hank Stram, former coach of the Kansas City Chiefs, has been reported as saying, "The important thing is to believe in something enough to make it work." This observation certainly applies to the selection of business strategy.

This factor of managerial style is critical in examining the role of R&D in a given business. The adoption of R&D as a principal weapon in the pursuit of growth inevitably involves risk. The existence of risk creates anxiety; and the individual attempting to make decisions when he is uncertain of his own judgment, when he feels he is sailing in strange waters, is not in a good position to make sound decisions. Moreover, he is less likely to have the self-confidence needed to provide the continuing support required to persist through adversity. Since the typical technical innovation is fraught with difficulties and blind alleys, a manager who feels uncomfortable in balancing technical risks and weighing alternatives is unlikely to emphasize technical innovation as a key ingredient in business strategy.

While the use of the word "intuition" may make businessmen uncomfortable, the fact remains that the most important business decisions are made intuitively. When it comes to the crunch, managers are forced to trust their intuition because they have run out of any other acceptable guide to action. Thus, a manager's intuitive feeling toward technological risk taking will play a critical role in determining whether or not he is favorably inclined toward aggressive use of R&D as an instrument of growth, and whether, having chosen to do so, he will provide it the support it needs.

Developing Intuition

How do managers form their intuition? While the process clearly involves a complex interaction between many factors, it is apparent that early formative work experience plays a crucial role. If a manager is not exposed early in his career to a business in which technological risk taking is a way of life, it is unlikely that he will himself opt for it later on. And as we will see later (Chapter 6) there are in many cases quite rational alternatives to technological risk taking as a basic business strategy.

The manager who has reached a position requiring business strategy formulation is at a level in the organization where he works almost exclusively with abstractions. The raw data involving physical, economic, social, and human facts have been filtered,classified, interpreted, and analyzed by many hands, each with a particular axe to grind as he contributed his input. These abstractions take on meaning for the man at the top only as he brings to bear his own experience and judgment, his own intuition, in interpreting them.

One can identify some of the features of judgment that are crucial in determining a manager's intuitive reaction toward the use of R&D as a principal instrument for growth and profitability. The most important element is undoubtedly a manager's sense of what constitutes the proper balance among the various functions required to conduct a business, especially among engineering, production, and marketing. While the relative emphasis given each of these functions is clearly heavily influenced by extrinsic competitive and technological considerations, the individual businessman still has great latitude within which to exercise his own discretion. The balance he seeks will be eventually determined by his intuitive feel for what is optimum; there is no objectively determined "right" answer.

Examples of companies that have succeeded dramatically or have maintained their competitive position by a strategy emphasizing innovative technological leadership are readily at hand, such as DuPont, Texas Instruments, and Syntex, among many others. There are companies that got into difficulty because they lost relative technological superiority or parity, and just as evident are companies that have succeeded by avoiding *any* pioneering in technology. One of the most impressive examples has been Emerson Electric Company, whose consistent growth over the past 15 years has earned a consistently high price/earnings ratio on Wall Street. W.R. Persons, the former chief executive officer who built the company, emphasizes that he did not invest in R&D in order to pioneer technically. The company's products are well designed and the product structure is shrewdly tailored to exploit attractive markets, but the products employ conventional technology. External consultants are used to provide guidance on major technical trends and developments. The lesson available from the experience of others is that whether the businessman chooses technical leadership or technical followership as his strategy, he ignores technical considerations at his own peril.

Another important element of intuitive judgment is a sense of the dynamics of a particular business. What is the natural time scale in which events in the business occur? Clearly, the situation in steel differs from that in aircraft, or foods, or plastics, or computers. A sense of dynamism acquired in one business can be frightfully wrong in another. In the raw materials and heavy equipment industries the normal planning horizon is years or even decades, and the pace of change is slow; in many consumer products the planning horizon may be only months; the pace of events in electronics frequently exceeds the response time of many companies. In many industries the flow of events is essentially a continuum, with one period merging imperceptibly into another; in others, activity is quantized into discrete parts (e.g., the model year in automobiles) and the "here and now" dominate everything. To a businessman conditioned to think in terms of six months to two years, an R&D proposal with a planned payoff seven to ten years later may be not only incomprehensible, but also irresponsible. Thus, intuition is specific in nature and one must be careful to establish the limits of the context in which one's intuition is applicable.

A third element of intuition is a sense of scale and proportion with respect to key business parameters, such as the dollar magnitudes involved, the physical volume (whether products are mass produced or one of a kind), the precision of measurement that is possible, the increments of change that are regarded as significant. An executive with a well-established background in large-scale custom-built apparatus exploded when first confronted with the in-process inventory required for a mass production business. The idea that a whole warehouse full of components was only a two-week inventory conflicted with his intuition. In power generation half-percent increases in efficiency are important and large changes will be suspect, while in aerospace an improvement by a factor of 2 or even an order of magnitude may be accepted as valid and precise measurement of small changes may be suspect. These differences with respect to scale may be critical in explaining why the aerospace industry has found it so difficult to succeed in the commercial world. Similarly, the incremental advances necessary for survival in computers are totally out of reach of more mature fields.

A fourth critical feature of intuition is a sense of sequencing and resource requirements. In what order should things be done? What things should be carried on in parallel and what things can be performed only in sequence? How long does it take to perform a given operation, how much work is involved, what kinds of resources and skills are required? The kind of knowledge that is required to answer questions of this type is acquired principally by experience. It produces a feel for a situation that gives the manager confidence that he is correctly "reading" the information that comes to him. He is particularly concerned with assessing its realism, and for this he must rely on somebody's judgment—his own or that of another with whom he is well attuned.

This kind of experience is exceedingly difficult to acquire when one is working with abstractions. Most managers build their intuitive feel for a business in their early formative years when they are themselves working with more tangible aspects of the business, irrespective of the functional area of interest. Whether it be in designing a product, making a market survey, locating and selling to specific customers, debugging a new line in the factory, or costing out a new process, the young future managers are living in a much more tangible world—a world of intractible data, missing information, incompatible inputs, and doubting Thomases in other functions, all the things that provide the rhythm of life in a business. Out of direct participation in this world the fledgling manager begins to formulate his sense of the business, his feel for what is realistic and what is unlikely, his ear for trouble. When he rises to positions that involve the formulation of policy and the specification of objectives, he will almost inevitably fall back on this intuition in his fundamental judgments about setting the course and pace of the business.

Managers whose formative experience provided little exposure to technological risk taking, who had no opportunity to see a technical discovery carried through to successful commercial application, are unlikely to feel comfortable when asked to approve such a course. More importantly, they are even less likely to single out technological innovation as a principal element of strategy.

Technological Risk Taking in Other Cultures

The consequences of this situation are perhaps most strikingly evident in observing the difficulties other countries are encountering in attempting to encourage more technological risk taking in industry. R&D has come to be accepted as so important to national growth and welfare that it has become an instrument of governmental policy. Consequently, many nations are developing explicit programs to encourage the growth of industrial investment in R&D. Many of these programs include special tax incentives, special write-offs on expenditures in R&D facilities, grants for specific R&D programs, loans, and commercial contracts tied to R&D efforts. All are intended to reduce the cost to the particular businessman of investing in R&D and to reduce the risk of such an investment. In addition, governments throughout the world, by their posture and by selective pressure, are reminding local businessmen of their responsibilities as good corporate citizens to contribute the vital technological strength needed. In spite of these inducements, progress has been disappointing.

Canada, for example, which has one of the oldest and most sophisticated government endeavors to stimulate and guide more industrial R&D, has modified national programs approximately every three years in an attempt to make them more effective. Canadian industrialists have a long tradition of business risk taking associated with mineral exploration and forest products. Young managers see risks of this kind being taken and success being achieved without great R&D support. A strategy of risk taking along such lines appears natural. Furthermore, the financial community also is familiar with such ventures, and mechanisms for providing the capital they need are at hand. In short, the Canadians know how to do these things and do them well.

Such a tradition is lacking in technology development. Much of Canada's technology has been imported through subsidiaries of foreign-owned companies. The local managers have grown up being taught, in effect, not to take technical risks, but rather to wait for the technical bugs to be worked out by the parent company and then to capitalize on the capability so developed. Not surprisingly, they are reluctant to formulate strategies featuring technological risk taking even when the government assumes most of the cost and strongly urges them to do so. Their intuitive judgment tells them this isn't the road to success. Furthermore, they feel uncertain in evaluating a technical proposal. What are the probabilities of technical success? How much money will it take? How long will it take? What kinds of resources are needed? Exactly what work has to be done to achieve the goal? Will it really give them a competitive edge? In all these areas they lack a basis on which to make judgments and thus defer their own involvement as much as possible.

In private discussions and in formal seminars with R&D managers, academicians, and government administrators in Western Europe, Japan, and Eastern Bloc countries, it is apparent that they firmly believe that American businessmen must have developed rigorous analytical techniques which minimize the necessity for personal faith and commitment in decision making on technical innovation. The willingness to embark on such uncertain waters in the absence of these anxiety-reducing methodologies obviously involves a point of view that they find mystifying and disturbing. They find it comforting to believe that our success in computers, nuclear energy, advanced aircraft, etc., is directly and solely attributable to careful planning and sophisticated analysis, since if this is the case they have only to acquire the methodology and then they can do likewise. The possibility that faith and a willingness to accept high risk for high rewards are key ingredients is not reassuring; in their minds the road to creating these attributes is a very murky one.

Of all the obstacles facing a country seeking to enlarge and strengthen its industrial technological base, this managerial gap resulting from lack of first-hand successful experience with technological innovation is probably the most intractable. We know very little about how people form their intuitive judgment, much less how they restructure it.

Restructuring Intuition

Phrased in this form the problem becomes one of much more general importance. One inevitable consequence of a general move toward institutionalizing the process of change is a speedup in the introduction of change and a general stiffening of the entire process, so that it is much less tolerant of mistakes and incompetence. Thus, we are creating a greater likelihood of what might be termed "intuitional obsolescence."[39] The consequences of a situation in which one's judgmental capabilities are unable to adjust rapidly enough to be applicable to matters requiring judgmental inputs are not attractive—anxiety, aberration, withdrawal, etc., are the result.

The little that is known about the developmental sequence for cognitive learning is not encouraging. The fragmentary evidence suggests that in many areas of learning, early experience is crucial and that there are sequences of development which essentially must be followed. It is known, for example, that people who have been born blind but later acquire the physiological capacity to see, experience great difficulty in actually learning to see. The effort required is enormous and the level of achievement is low. For example, they tend to confuse shapes such as triangles and rectangles.

Similarly, in the realm of science one can observe the consequences of revolutions in its conceptual structure such as was caused by the development of quantum mechanics in physics. Many of the physicists who had already acquired their inventory of conceptual tools before the advent of quantum mechanics had the competence to go back and to learn the formalisms associated with quantum mechanics. Even when they acquired some facility in manipulating the mathematics associated with it, they rarely incorporated it into the collection of techniques with which to conduct their research. In contrast, physicists who were still creating their conceptual tools at the time, and those coming later, use quantum mechanics almost unthinkingly as one of the tools of research. The difference is most obvious in the crucial region of perceiving problems and choosing methods of attack. For the post-quantum mechanics physicists it's a quantum mechanics world; they start from that point in looking for interesting research problems, in generating data, and in interpreting results. The older physicist is more likely to perceive problems from a base in classical physics.

I suspect we are seeing a very similar phenomenon today in the revolution being created in information processing, only this time the involvement is much greater and the implications are much more widespread. Virtually the entire realm of the professions, including management itself, is facing the challenge of acquiring facility in using a new conceptual tool. I predict that it will never become second nature to those attempting to learn about information processing in mid-career. By that I do not require that they achieve technical mastery over the computer itself, but simply that they incorporate the capability it provides into their conception of the nature of their work and of how to make effective progress.

The implications of this problem for management are profound, and argue strongly against the utility of "quickie" courses to give people superficial knowledge of new tools and new concepts that appear after their own conceptual apparatus was formed, with the expectation that the graduates will apply the new tools. The objective of mid-career education must be to acquire enough knowledge to have the self-confidence to at least turn to the experts for help, to ask sensible questions of these experts, to weigh the answers critically, and to avoid being defensive about one's limited knowledge. These latter two points are particularly important. As *The Economist*[38] pointed out in evaluating the data processing industry, a businessman must be just as hardheaded in demanding specific objectives and anticipated benefits from data processing as he would be in appraising any other investment. He must not let the protagonist for data processing "snow" him with esoteric terminology and vaguely defined concepts.

It is likely that awareness of the growing force of this problem of coping with rapid change underlies the greater emphasis that is coming to be placed on, and the higher status attached to, staff activities in speculations about the future of management and organization structure in industry. Seeking greater competence in, and according higher status to, staff specialists is one way of building a management team that explicitly makes provision for incorporating change into its behavior and its decision-making apparatus. This staff can serve to expand the collective intuition of senior executives by helping to characterize and clarify the intuition itself. Intimate contact with management but a certain detachment from its decision making are necessary for such characterization. Psychologists have long known that realistic and perceptive self-awareness is a key ingredient in maintaining emotional health. The same applies to the management of a firm. A realistic appraisal of what the management is good at and what it is poorly equipped for, and of its capacity for adaptation, is a crucial element in the formulation of corporate strategy. The difficulties of some of the overextended conglomerates in the late 1960s provided a painful reminder of the need for such awareness.

The implications with respect to incorporating technological innovation as a major element of business strategy are quite clear. If this course is to be adopted and pursued successfully, at least some of the key managers at the top of the organization must have early exposure to a business environment in which technological innovation is indeed a way of life. They must have seen technical risks being taken, they must have had direct first-hand contact with some part of the tangible world that has created successful technological innovation. If we are to be successful in our endeavors to institutionalize the creation of change through technology, we must make early exposure to technical innovation a prerequisite for a significant fraction of the senior management of an organization.

The emergence of the concept of an executive office is a recognition of the need to retain diversity of point of view at the top of a company. This diversity of background and of temperament is another way of enlarging the collective intuition of management. If R&D managers can grow beyond advocacy to seek integration they may find that they will be entrusted with broader responsibility to create innovation throughout the company.

Summary

This chapter has examined the corporate context in which innovation occurs. It has stressed the pressure for results and the requirement for certainty in performance which can lead the businessman to eschew innovation. It has examined the role of managerial style as an important ingredient in the formulation of strategy. Successful managers can choose to run businesses in many different ways, and technological innovation need not be one of them. Which strategy a manager adopts will depend on which he feels most confident about undertaking. The effect of his early work experience in developing his managerial intuition will be a key factor in his decision-making apparatus. The chapter concludes by considering some of the sobering implications of the intuitional obsolescence that too rapid change can create.

6

Alternatives to Technological Innovation in Business Strategy

The discussion thus far has begun to explore the procedures required if we are to succeed in institutionalizing the creation of change, of creating a viable new function for innovation. The need for R&D managers to move beyond advocacy and special pleading is a necessary first step. If this step is to succeed, the total organization must be structured in such a way as to nurture innovation, and must provide means of achieving a suitable balance between risk and reward. Even more important is the requirement to insure adequate management attention to the long-run time frame that must be associated with successful innovation, attention achieved only by making it the primary responsibility of high-status executives.

Of equal importance in the move toward closer integration of R&D with the business is the need for R&D managers to recognize the milieu in which business executives work. The pressures for ever-improving performance are a severe barrier to accepting the risk and uncertainty inherent in innovation. Furthermore, relatively few senior executives have had direct personal experience with technological risk taking during their formative years. The R&D manager must come to appreciate that these men are not necessarily unsympathetic to technological innovation, nor do they lack courage, but that they may frequently face situations with which they are poorly equipped to deal.

In order to be successful in institutionalizing change through technological innovation, it will be necessary for technological goals to be built into business strategy and for experience with this kind of activity to be built into the management team. We must achieve the situation in which research and development is regarded not as a separate, largely autonomous activity, but rather as one of the fundamental activities that a successful business performs in order to grow and prosper. This is not to say that successful R&D requires the surrender of all autonomy. All business functions—engineering, manufacturing, marketing, finance—maintain considerable autonomy in their internal operations, but they all work within the constraints imposed by the specific goals and needs of the business. An indispensable step in seeking to incorporate research and development goals into business strategy is to be able to understand, in a very unromanticized way, the alternatives to an emphasis on technology which a businessman may perceive when he considers questions of strategy. R&D managers need to understand the various options available to the executive as he pursues profitable growth in the operation of his business. They must also recognize the fact that for each of the options available as a strategy for growth, there may indeed be very attractive alternatives to research and development for implementing these options.

Business Strategy Options

Basically, all business strategies are built up of varying combinations of four fundamental options. The first and most limited, of course, is the situation where little opportunity for attractive growth is perceived and the preferred strategy is to optimize the generation of profits from an essentially stable business. Under this strategy of harvesting, the manager will make additional investments primarily to optimize return over the remaining life of the business, which may cover a very long time span.

Second, the manager can attempt growth of the business in its current form, seeking increased profitability and/or increased market penetration by selling more of the same products to the same customers or to new customers, but in the same markets and channels of distribution, and by serving the same general function as far as the customer is concerned. Under this option the business would become larger, but its basic character would be unchanged. Most of the battling among the food, soap, appliance, and automobile companies is of this character.

Third, he can use the present business as a base to exploit associated opportunities; i.e., he will extend the business. These opportunities will usually take one of three forms: (1) adding new products (not just additional models or styles of present products) or product lines so as to take advantage of *marketing strengths* in serving present markets or in penetrating new geographical markets, as Maytag did in adding dishwashers to its product lines; (2) modifying or improving products so as to serve wider markets or new customers and thus taking advantage of *technical strengths*, as General Electric did in entering the commercial jet engine business; and (3) undertaking vertical integration so as to move closer to the ultimate customer or to basic raw materials, as Polaroid did in building its own film manufacturing facilities. In each of these cases the fundamental character of the business would be altered in a visible, tangible manner, but in such a fashion as to capitalize on some key strengths of the original business.

Fourth, the manager may try to create a new business by using managerial skills and perhaps the financial and human resources available in his present business to do so. This diversification may be accomplished by acquisition of another company, by attaining access to needed technology or marketing know-how through licensing or forming a joint venture, or it may be done by growing a business from the ground up, based on inventions created inside the organization. The dramatic growth of ITT by acquisition is a classical example of such diversification, relying principally on managerial skills and financial resources.

Harvesting Present Business

The implementation of a business strategy aimed at harvesting is more challenging than one might first think. Its specific features depend on the time scale of the harvest mode and the competitive position of the business as well as on the specific functional efforts the manager chooses to emphasize. With respect to time scale, it is important to note—given the future prospects of the market and the present position of the company—that, at the minimum, choosing this strategy simply says that no effort will be directed to the further growth of the business, but that the time horizon for action may be many years long. The term optimum clearly implies the investment of the additional resources necessary to insure the best possible return from hard-won competitive advantages that may already have been established in cost, product leadership, and customer loyalty. Nevertheless, this type of strategy is clearly peripheral to the central thrust of our discussion with respect to institutionalizing the creation of change, and therefore will receive no further treatment.

Growing the Present Business

With respect to the second option, growing the present business, it is apparent, except in a monopolistic situation, that the businessman must seek to be better or to appear to be better than his competitors with regard to cost, performance, quality, features, and service. Therefore, if he chooses the option of growing the present business, he will put great emphasis on reducing costs; on improving the performance of his product with respect to life, efficiency, reliability, convenience, etc.; or on achieving product differentiation through special features, styling, service, etc. At first glance it might appear, particularly to those inclined toward a technical orientation, that there is no better way to pursue these objectives than through aggressive exploitation of technology which, after all, can have an impact on each. If we are to appreciate the businessman's perspective, however, we must consider what other means he may have available to achieve exactly these same ends and how these alternatives may compare in attractiveness with technology, with attractiveness being evaluated by three criteria: (1) how much it will cost; (2) how long it will take to put into operation; and (3) what the risk of failure is.

Cost reduction is one area in which technological innovation clearly offers great promise. New materials such as plastics may be inherently cheaper or may permit less expensive designs. New devices such as transistors may be less expensive or require less power to operate. New understanding of phenomena may permit greater efficiency or reduce the stresses in jet engines. In fact, one of the most important contributions of technological innovation is in reducing the manufacturing and operating cost of products. Nevertheless, the protagonist for technology would be wise to recognize that, through the eyes of the businessman, there are other exceedingly attractive, and in many cases much more certain, ways of achieving cost reductions than through advanced technology programs, which frequently appear to be lengthy, costly, and uncertain of success. Some of these alternatives are quite far removed from technology.

For example, high fixed costs increasingly characterize today's business operations and it is apparent that any increase in volume can have a significant effect on unit cost. Consequently, even shrewd pricing can have the effect of a cost reduction if it succeeds in raising volume sufficiently. Similarly, an advertising campaign that significantly increases volume can reduce costs. An aggressive program to provide the business with strong, capable distributors who get a larger share of the given market in a geographic area can also significantly affect volume and costs.

Manufacturing and distribution cost can sometimes be reduced by restructuring the product line to reduce the number of models produced and sold. Improved plant and warehouse location can effect a cost reduction by lowering transportation charges and reducing capital costs. Even direct shop costs can be reduced by means other than application of technology. For example, labor productivity can be improved by installing new machinery, or by improved supervision, or by greater commitment by workers, or by training that reduces absenteeism and improves quality. The list could easily be extended.

The important point to appreciate is that, in the eyes of the businessman, all these alternatives may in fact be more attractive than the pursuit of technology as a way to reduce costs. They may be areas in which he can plan and forecast with more precision, in which the money required to accomplish the necessary improvement is smaller, and in which the total time required for payoff is significantly less than that required for a cost reduction through technology. The technical man working in research and development is in most cases not brought in contact with these other options and is typically only dimly aware of the fact that the businessman has them available to consider. As a consequence, he may frequently not perceive that the businessman is not opposed to research and development nor is he unwilling to spend money in this area. It is just that, in his judgment, there are clearly better ways to spend the firm's funds to achieve the objective of profitable growth through cost reduction.

The same conditions apply in considering the various alternatives that add up to product differentiation, whether they be product improvement, special features, or life. Again, from the standpoint of the businessman, a number of attractive alternatives to the use of technology may be available as a way of achieving product differentiation. Color, configuration, and style are especially pertinent in the case of consumer goods, and their dependence on technology is frequently remote. Service—the availability of parts, the availability of a wide variety of models to choose from, rapid delivery, quick repair—can constitute a significant aspect of product differentiation in the eyes of the consuming public, but has limited dependence on technology. The sophisticated industrial buyer is just as interested in service; quick supply of parts, rapid response to problems, rapid delivery, certainty of production—all weigh heavily in choices made by the industrial buyer. Advertising can be used to create product differentiation simply by changing the customer's perception of the nature of the product, or even by changing his own self-image.

The protagonist for technology may argue that some of these differences are ephemeral or trivial, but they are no less real to the businessman and their impact on profits can be just as tangible as that generated by technology. The crucial point once again is that, from the standpoint of the businessman, there may be alternatives for achieving product differentiation that cost less money, that are more certain of success, and that require less time to carry through to fruition.

In seeking profitable growth through improved product performance, the businessman is, of course, placing reliance on continuing technical advance. This type of contribution has been the traditional forte of technological innovation, and it is certainly the role that most technical people visualize for innovation. When an engineer says that a business is not technology limited, he really means that he already knows how to design products whose performance is adequate to satisfy present and forecasted customer requirements; he rarely equates technology directly with lower cost. However, as the Japanese are showing the world, it is not necessary to pioneer in improving performance through internally generated technological innovation in order to achieve remarkable competitive success. It is frequently possible to purchase the needed technology and focus internal efforts on application.

This point is important to understand and it should not be interpreted as depreciating the magnitude of the Japanese accomplishment. Two areas of dramatic Japanese impact have been in consumer electronics and electronic desk calculators. In both instances the advances in electronic componentry and in display technology, which made possible the design of the products, were developed in the United States. The Japanese demonstrated great skill in characterizing the market opportunity and in developing products to exploit it, but the *technical* risk in what they did was slight. MITI, the Japanese ministry for international trade, has been urging Japanese firms to undertake more pioneering technical development because it is concerned about Japanese dependence on foreign technology for basic advances. Japanese industrialists have been slow to respond, preferring to continue to purchase technology as needed. One might conclude that United States firms have been selling their technology too cheaply; otherwise, the "make-buy" decision would not so consistently turn out to be "buy." There are increasing indications that the Japanese may be gradually shifting their effort to undertake a larger fraction of pioneering technical work.

Extending the Present Business

The third option of business strategy is to extend the present business into new areas, either by selling new products to old markets or by selling old or modified products to new markets. Here it might seem that the case for technology as a principal weapon of attack is more convincing. Nevertheless, careful examination indicates that, once again, attractive alternatives are available to the businessman. With respect to selling new products to old markets, new products can indeed be designed and manufactured from internally generated technology, but they may also be acquired simply by purchasing the existing manufacturer, as Emerson Electric has typically done, or by buying the product itself and relying on one's power in distribution and marketing, as in the case of Sears-Roebuck.

Another possibility under this option of selling old or modified products to new markets may involve no more than geographic expansion to acquire distributors and salesmen in areas in which the company has not been previously active. This move creates a strong challenge to marketing and finance, but leaves technology virtually untouched. Alternatively, this move may involve extending the product offering to new types of customers, as in the case of selling appliances to the rapidly growing mobile-home market. Such a move calls for identifying a new class of customer, perhaps developing a new type of salesman to deal with it. Certainly a new pricing structure and probably even a modified product line will be necessary to meet the customer's particular needs, but the requirements for technological innovation are minimal.

Even when the decision to enter a new associated market involves the development of special products to serve a new application, it frequently involves no more than the use of technology already available rather than the development of new technology. The need is to focus the technology so as to meet the requirements of a new class of customer who may demand special features such as unusual precision, reliability, fast response, and stability. This would be the case of electric motors for tape drives for computers; or conversely, lower cost, less sophistication, shorter life, lower performance, and very small size as in the case of electric motors for toys. The technical implications of the decision of whether or not to make the move may be small compared with other factors such as building distribution channels, amount of investment required, reaction of competitors, government regulation, management talent available. Even building codes and union practices can be critical factors if one is contemplating the construction market.

A third possibility for extending the business involves vertical integration, either backward toward raw materials or forward toward the ultimate user. A move in either of these directions will almost certainly involve technology that, though new to the firm, already exists. For example, there are occasional rumors of major chemical companies going into oil refining in order to seek economic advantage by producing their own petrochemical feedstocks. The technology of oil refining is already highly developed, even though it is foreign to chemical companies. Thus, while the company presumably has the option of developing a technological innovation that could give a proprietary advantage in vertical integration, it typically has the option of acquiring the technical information needed, either by purchase of another company or by a licensing agreement.

The technologist naturally tends to look with great favor on vertical integration based on proprietary technology, and the leverage of such an approach has been demonstrated by Dow Chemical. But here again, he must remember the tyranny of certainty, which was discussed earlier. The businessman is exceedingly concerned over the consequences of failing to achieve his objective; he never escapes the unforgiving environment for American industry today. The man involved in developing new technology assumes as a matter of course that there will be many trials and tribulations, that there will be false starts, points at which progress seems stymied, times when schedules may slip or objectives must be lowered to what is attainable. He accepts this as part of the game in R&D. On the other hand, to the businessman these are problems he must avoid if he possibly can because they create uncertainty and thus create the risk that his plans and projections may not be realized. We must never forget that technical risk is not the only risk involved in attempting a technological innovation. Therefore, an entrepreneur tends to look with much more favor on technical processes that have already been worked out by others because they remove at least one element of uncertainty.

Even the purchase of technology is fraught with risk. Technical people all too frequently fail to make adequate allowance for the exceedingly difficult problem of acquiring *all* relevant information associated with a technology that is new to the organization. Even though technology is already widely practiced by other organizations, there is an inevitable period of stumbling and of learning as one puts the technology to work in one's own organization. Indeed, manufacturing people who have attempted to start up new plants using entirely old technology, but with new workers, are well aware of the trials and tribulations involved in creating a truly reliable operation. The businessman starts out with what is for him a very well-founded suspicion of any attempt to develop a proprietary position based on new technology, when he already knows he will have trouble enough simply applying old technology.

Creating a New Business

The fourth strategic option for growth is to create entirely new businesses in which the technology, the markets, and the customers are new. The past 15 years have demonstrated very forcibly that there are attractive ways to achieve this end through acquisition rather than through the development of proprietary technology. The growth of the conglomerates has demonstrated that shrewd financial manipulation may in fact be a much more rapid path to diversified growth than is the development of technology. The widespread use of licensing as a basis for acquiring capability to go into entirely new businesses represents another alternative that many firms would prefer to exploit, if at all possible, because again from their point of view it reduces the risk. In the case where a firm chooses to create new businesses by creating new products, it frequently has the option of acquiring the crucial aspects of technology by the purchase of components and can thus focus its attention on appearance design or systems configuration. As noted above, the Japanese electronic desk calculators made extensive use of integrated circuit modules manufactured in the United States.

In some situations a firm has the option of going the low technology route rather than the high technology route when contemplating a new opportunity. For example, in deciding to go into a line of audio equipment for the home, rather than emphasize technical perfection in the reproduction of sound, one may choose to emphasize the design of attractive audio furniture components so that they appeal to the housewife, or are easy to assemble, or are easy to incorporate into the home. These and other similar possibilities minimize the amount of technical effort and the technical risk that must be incurred. Surprisingly, the creation of a new product or a new business frequently makes no particular demands on technology, but grows out of the perception of a need and the design of a particular configuration to satisfy it. For example, the craze for snowmobiles provided an opportunity to serve a need in a rapidly growing new business, but the creation of the product did not require significant development of new technology. The creative contribution lay in perceiving the need and adapting existing technology to satisfy it.

This examination of alternatives to technology as a vehicle for growth is not meant to suggest that technology is not an exceedingly attractive option. It is simply to put the perspective of the businessman in better focus and to remind the enthusiastic scientist or engineer that there are indeed alternative ways to achieve many of the same objectives for which he sees technology as the most attractive route. Furthermore, in the eyes of the man who has to put up the money and who has to assume the risk, these other alternatives may in many cases be more attractive. If for no other reason than to know the competition, technical people who are seeking to insure that research and development has more influence in the formulation of business strategy should become aware of the perspective from which business strategy is formulated. Even more, they should be aware of the alternative options that are available and of the competition that technology must face in seeking designation as a principal element of the thrust for growth.

If the manager of research and development who is seeking to incorporate challenging technical objectives into business strategy is to be successful, he must be realistic in appraising the competition that he faces. Also he must be realistic in recognizing that in many cases, if he were making the decision, he would choose not to emphasize technological innovation as the route to profitable growth. If he persists in a kind of blind advocacy of the technical alternative in the face of these other clear options, which in the eyes of the decision maker may be more attractive, he simply demonstrates to others that he does not yet appreciate the facts of life in business. Consequently, he will continue to be regarded as one whose judgment is not to be trusted in the crucial area of charting the strategy for the future of the business.

Summary

A businessman has four basic strategic options available: harvest, grow the business in the present form, extend it into associated areas, and create a new business. For each option, technology can be a principal mode of implementation. It is important to recognize, however, that there are other modes of implementation, which frequently involve less expense, less risk, and less time to come to fruition. Recognition of the alternatives helps to explain the apparent bias against technology which many infer from business decisions. It also provides a more realistic basis for arguing the case for the technological alternative—the goal of the R&D manager.

7　Impact of Technology on Business

Every field of endeavor develops its own special concepts, its own private terminology. This private language becomes a kind of shorthand for insiders. It includes not only the technical terms needed in the work, but also classification systems, status symbols, and descriptions of relationships. Not surprisingly, most of the terminology and concepts that have been developed to facilitate discourse in the world of research and development have been developed by insiders themselves. As one would expect, the terms they use and the classification systems that they have developed do provide a quick shorthand for communicating about what they regard as the most significant activities involved in research and development. This terminology is used by insiders not only to discuss work among themselves, but also in their attempts to communicate with people outside R&D regarding the nature of research and development, its relationship to other activities, and its impact on events outside research and development itself. While the obvious intent is to aid communication, these terms and classification systems have sometimes been the cause of a good deal of difficulty, even among insiders themselves.

Probably the most general classification system devised to describe the work that goes on in research and development is represented by the terms "basic research," "applied research," and "development." These terms encompass the entire spectrum of R&D work and are intended to imply something about the character of the work being done, the nature of its relationship to other kinds of work, and the implications of these three classes of work for society itself. That the task is not easy is amply demonstrated by the almost endless arguments about the boundary between the various classes of work and whether a particular kind of work belongs in one classification or the other.

Among other things, these three classifications are intended to provide a way of giving some indication of the extent of "practicality" of the work being done and of the likelihood of its having a specific commercial impact. Unfortunately, the connotations that are intended by these three classifications may be difficult for the businessman to fit into his own planning framework. It would be very helpful to him if a description of what goes on in research and development could be presented from the perspective of an external observer rather than that of an insider, one that approached the question from the standpoint of the risk taker who will be investing in the work rather than that of the technical man who will be performing the work. If such a system could be developed, it would be much more likely to provide a means for the businessman to incorporate the proposals of research and development into his overall business planning and to use the same judgment and analysis that he applies in examining other aspects of the operation of the firm.

Classifying R&D in Terms of Risk

One way of approaching this problem is to try to separate the problem of classification into two separate phases. The current system of terminology, basic research, applied research, and development attempts to do two things at the same time. First, it attempts to describe the point of view of the individual performing work at various stages in the process and to suggest the flow of work through the spectrum. Second, it attempts to convey to laymen the social or commercial implications of what is being done at various stages. It may help if the R&D task itself (i.e., what goes on inside the R&D function) is essentially regarded as a "black box." It is important for insiders to be aware of the intricacies of what goes on in the black box and to develop sophisticated classification systems to characterize the nature of the work inside the box. But the businessman is principally interested in what comes out of the box and in being able to evaluate its implications for his business. In a sense he doesn't care whether the work is basic, or applied, or developmental, especially since he isn't sure of the meaning of those terms anyway. Probably the most meaningful descriptors to the decision maker are those that characterize the *output* of R&D in terms of the risk inherent in the work; i.e., in terms of the probability of success or failure and of the accuracy of the estimates with respect to time required for completion and the resources necessary to accomplish the objectives.

Approached in this way, the output of research and development can be divided into three major classifications: (1) work that involves applying the state-of-the-art conventional technology; (2) work that involves extending the state-of-the-art; and (3) work that involves development or application of new technology. In every case the point of view here is that of the investor, the man who will be trying to take advantage of the output of R&D rather than that of the people who are performing it. Thus, the term "new" here implies new to the user of technology and not necessarily new to the producer of technology. The businessman may, quite properly I believe, be wary of being asked to invest in technology that already exists but which his company has not previously applied. He will no doubt discover that learning how to use available technology includes its own risks and unanticipated problems.

Applying the State-of-the-Art

The term "state-of-the-art" is widely used in technical work. One of the questions the patent examiner must answer is whether or not a particular invention represents an advance in the state-of-the-art, the state-of-the-art being the knowledge, concepts, methodology, and techniques that any man trained in a particular profession would be expected to know and be able to apply. Most technical work involves just this kind of activity, i.e., application of the state-of-the-art. While it may indeed involve conceiving new configurations, applying products to areas not previously exploited, providing features not previously available, or developing products not previously available, the fact is that having conceived of the need to provide a particular capability or service the technical means for doing so are in many cases already at hand. As a matter of fact, a variety of technical means may be at hand, and the principal question may be which combination of options is optimum. Consequently, for the cases in which application of state-of-the-art technology is what is needed, judgments on costs, volume, and customer desires are more important than technical judgment.

This is not to say that there is not ample opportunity for the demonstration of technical ingenuity and creativity in putting together particular configurations to serve a perceived need. Much skilled engineering goes into work of this kind. The point is that the technical risk involved is exceedingly low. The man who is saying, "Should I invest money in this proposition?" can be given answers with considerable assurance and precision to questions regarding what is possible, how long it will take to perform the work, how much and what kinds of resources will be necessary to accomplish the task, and even what technical options are available from which to choose. Risks still exist with respect to attainable levels of cost and whether, having accomplished the technical and cost objectives, the product will in fact turn out to be a commercial success.

Interestingly enough, application of the state-of-the-art is not limited to what one might regard as simple or unsophisticated technologies. Indeed, some of the most sophisticated work done in our society involves the application of state-of-the-art technology which has been highly developed over many years and has become so esoteric that extensive training and experience are required to become an effective practitioner, as in the structural design of bridges and large buildings and in the practice of medicine. In fact, application of the state-of-the-art is the principal component of all engineering work—even in our most advanced space systems —because it rests on a huge base of prior knowledge. As an art matures it attains greater and greater precision and approaches the physical limits of the materials and phenomena involved. Consequently, its application demands a high degree of specialization. We are surrounded by complicated machinery that works so remarkably well that we tend to forget the tremendous array of knowledge required to design and manufacture the equipment we use daily. A company contemplating an international expansion recently calculated that it would require seven very large volumes to describe the specifications and the design together with the manufacturing instructions for *one* refrigerator model.

The field of research and development does not lack for unfortunate value connotations regarding the attractiveness or the merit of particular kinds of work. The tendency to emphasize the new and the startling as being the most important and the most prized is one of the most unfortunate such status distinctions. Application of state-of-the-art is also the largest single activity involved in research and development. This assertion may come as a shock to practitioners of R&D, but a moment's reflection will remind them that the methodology of research itself is a state-of-the-art. As Kuhn[51, 52,] has pointed out, even basic research is an affirmation of the validity of the methodology of science and much basic research is an attempt to make small improvements in that methodology. Much of development is the work required to select and prove out the most cost-effective solution to a problem rather than to invent a solution.

State-of-the-art technology can be applied to any of the business strategies discussed in Chapter 6. Thus, efforts to grow the present business by reducing cost, by improving performance, and by adding new features, to a very substantial extent lend themselves to the use of state-of-the-art technology. Costs are reduced because one discovers that unnecessary safety margins can be eliminated from designs, that materials with better properties than are necessary are being used, that the use of a different process would give a lower cost or a higher yield in manufacturing or would involve less trouble on the shop floor. Similarly, an ingenious engineer may find a way to add a new feature based on a well-known concept or technique in engineering and using readily available materials.

While it may be less obvious, a strategy of extending the present business into new areas also frequently involves principally the application of the state-of-the-art. The critical question is whether or not the firm will choose to commit its resources to a strategy aimed at extension rather than growth in present markets, and this decision is primarily a business decision. If one chooses, for example, to develop a special line of electric motors for use in the automotive industry, or in the computer industry where the cost and performance standards are very different, the technology for doing so in either case is largely at hand. As a matter of fact, in many cases competing products may already be available. The critical evaluation for the businessman is the answer to the commercial question of whether or not it can be done at a cost that will permit profitable sale. This problem involves not only the engineering estimate on costs but also estimates of the volume that the firm can achieve, the nature of the manufacturing techniques and processes available, the suitability and availability of the labor force, the effectiveness of distribution; many other things besides the technical features themselves will affect the final cost of the product as delivered to the customer.

Similarly, as noted in Chapter 6, the development of entirely new products for new businesses does not necessarily require new inventions or the development of new technology. The critical advance may be in perceiving a new need or a new opportunity and in selecting the most effective available technology in developing a product that will serve that need in a fashion which profitably matches costs with perceived value by the customer. One of the most common mistakes made in developing a product is to provide more performance capability than the customer is willing to pay for. The electric knife is an interesting example of an extension of a business (housewares) by creating a new product to go through existing distribution channels in its presentation to customers. The knife required creative engineering in conceiving and executing an effective design, but there was very little technical risk in the work and the technology was virtually all at hand. The principal advance was in perceiving the opportunity and in committing the resources to perform the development.

Extending the State-of-the-Art

The second class of technical work involves an extension or an advance in the state-of-the-art. Work of this type falls generally into three subclasses: refinements in design, advances in materials and processes, and improvements in the engineering tools themselves. Refinements in design leading to lower cost and/or improved performance can result from a great variety of engineering improvements. These improvements may be in learning how to reduce or make more uniform the stresses materials are exposed to. This knowledge can either reduce the amount of material required or increase life. Changes in design can simplify manufacturing and reduce cost as well as improve quality. Improving heat transfer will permit higher operating temperatures and thus extend the working range of materials. Most of the work classification system should be output oriented. The familiar classification of basic research, applied research, and the development does not fit these criteria. The terms may have some value inside the R&D organization, but they are not helpful to the businessman.

Properties of materials are constantly being improved by major materials vendors so as to make them stronger, less susceptible to corrosion, more heat resistant, flame resistant, etc. For example, improvements of magnetic steels over the years have played an important role in improving transformer performance and in increasing power density, thus permitting increases in capacity without increasing size. Similarly, processes can be improved to reduce cycle times, to increase yields, and to reduce rejects. An alert engineering organization will seek ways to incorporate these improvements into the design so as to reduce size and weight, increase performance, improve reliability, etc.

Work carried on to improve engineering tools is less obvious in its impact on the product, but very important nevertheless. Work of this type is aimed at such things as better measurement, which gives the engineer more detailed and precise knowledge regarding product operation; computer programs for design calculations, which permit examination of a greater range of design alternatives and provide solutions that are closer to optimum; test facilities, which better simulate actual performance conditions; or better scientific understanding of the phenomena that are operative in the product or in the environment in which the product functions, such as knowledge of the behavior of materials, of dielectric breakdown, of the mechanisms of corrosion, etc. All these up-to-date tools improve engineering productivity, reduce the time required to develop and introduce new products, and lead to designs that are tighter, provide more reliable products, and are better matched to customer requirements.

In technical work of these various kinds the level of risk is clearly higher than is the case with applying conventional technology. Nevertheless, in most such situations qualified technical people can still give a reasonable estimate as to whether or not something is possible of attainment. They can even estimate the probabilities of success over a range of levels of attainment. It is more difficult for them to estimate how much time it will take to attain the objectives and how much investment will be required. Consequently, the businessman must recognize that the estimates being given to him for completing a task involving extension of the state-of-the-art have more uncertainty with respect to the time and the cost required. Incorporating work of this sort into a tight schedule involving coordination with work in manufacturing or marketing also involves more uncertainty and indicates the need for close managerial control. A slippage in schedule can mean not only spiraling costs but also a loss of market potential, where timing is critical to market success.

Activity devoted to extending the state-of-the-art generally involves the next largest level of effort after application of conventional technology. Extension of state-of-the-art can also have impact across the spectrum of strategy options for business growth, such as improving the present business, extending into new markets or new products, or growing a new business. Its impact on improving the present business is obvious, but an extension in technology can also permit cost reductions or improvements in performance which permit one to serve new markets; for example, improving the flame resistance of a plastic so that it can be used in the building industry; improving the corrosion resistance of a jet engine so that it can be used in a marine environment; and improving the processing of integrated circuits so that yield from manufacture is increased and costs are reduced, thus opening up markets in consumer products. Such extensions can also provide the key step in entering a new business; say, in using advances in integrated circuitry and display to enter the personal calculator market, as Texas Instruments has done.

Developing New Technology

The third category of work involves developing or applying new technology, including early exploration of an idea to demonstrate technical and economic feasibility for a particular application. Work of this kind is most closely identified in the layman's eyes with the true meaning of research and development. Practitioners of R&D have undoubtedly fostered this attitude by emphasizing this aspect of the work; it is more glamorous, it is more attention-getting, and of course it is the area from which the spectacular advances come. Nevertheless, in our effort to look at R&D through the eyes of a potential investor, we must look behind the glamour. It soon becomes apparent that this classification includes two distinct subsets: work on new technologies that will accomplish a function which is already performed by some other means, and the invention of technologies that provide a new function, a new service to society. These subsets are so different that they must be treated separately.

New Technology Applied to Established Function.   In the first case the impact of the new technology will be largely substitutional: The function performed by the product remains the same, but the physical process by which the function is performed is altered significantly or the physical embodiment of the product is radically different. The introduction of solid-state electronics is the most widely acclaimed substitution example since World War II. Since society already had available a means of accomplishing the given function, it is apparent that the new technology had to demonstrate its superiority over present methods through lower cost or by providing some form of greater value such as improved performance, reduced size, convenience, or reliability. The present enthusiastic acceptance of solid-state components implies that they have satisfied most, if not all, criteria for many applications. The crucial distinction is that success is based on our judgment of economic value, not on the technical elegance of the development. Nevertheless, of all the effort devoted to developing new technology, the success of a great majority of it lies in its supplanting a conventional technology.

While the emphasis on the substitutional impact of new technology may seem to rob R&D of some of its glamour, we must not lose sight of its enormous social and economic impact. One *should* expect a sophisticated, highly technological society such as ours to have the capability to accomplish most of the things we want to accomplish (medical treatment is a notable exception because we still do not know how to predict, treat, and/or prevent diseases such as cancer and heart attacks). The key to continuing progress and prosperity is to find ways to lower costs and improve performance. In fact, all technological progress must pass the test of value as perceived by the user and thus must be cost-competitive. The ubiquitous nature of this economic criterion is frequently ignored by those caught up in the excitement of developing a new technology. Examples of this form of technological substitution are legion and some go quite far back in history: open hearth for Bessemer steel furnaces, margarine for butter, latex for oil-base paints, jet engines for propeller-driven planes.

It is not surprising that this type of technological innovation is frequently described as technological "invasion." It is not an everyday occurrence, nor does the substitution occur rapidly. The normal pattern is for the initial application to be one in which the special properties of the new technology have great leverage or where the new approach overcomes a significant limitation in conventional technology. The use of integrated circuits in space computers is a good example. The advantages of size and weight reduction and faster response compensate for their typically high initial cost and unproven life. As time goes on, the reliability of the new technology is increased, costs come down, designers learn how to compensate for its shortcomings, and less exotic applications can be justified. Eventually, the "new" technology pushes out the traditional methods from virtually all applications.

This type of technological advance is rarely discovered by people who are seeking to apply or extend the current state-of-the-art. In the great majority of cases the new technology requires skills different from those associated with the conventional technology. As a result, the practitioners of the conventional technology inevitably acquire a valued investment in their particular skills and develop a protective attitude toward the significance and utility of the technology they apply. Consequently, it is difficult for them to acquire the dedication and vision necessary to create their own revolution. To the contrary, the new technical option is more likely to be resisted strenuously as a threat to status and livelihood. The classical confrontation between vacuum tubes and solid-state electronics—a confrontation that is entering its third decade—is well known. The confrontation is being repeated in the battle between microwave tubes and solid-state devices, and between electromechanical and solid-state techniques for converting electric power from alternating to direct current. In a very different arena a confrontation is developing between gas turbines on the one hand and both diesel engines and steam turbines on the other as prime movers for marine propulsion. In each of these instances the new technology is not developed by the practitioners of the prevailing state-of-the-art.

These advances are also frequently the result of the supply-push type of invention arising out of the creative efforts of people seeking major advances in technology without regard to specific applications. The laser is a good example. Many of its applications will be substitutional, but its inventor was not trying to solve these specific problems.

The technical risk associated with this type of work is much higher than that in either applying or extending the state-of-the-art. The identification of initial applications in which the unique advantages of the new technology can have greatest leverage may be crucial to its successful introduction. The only trouble is that, as a fledgling technology, many of its characteristics have yet to be identified. Thus, many unknowns must be risked in its early applications. Nevertheless, technological innovations of this type frequently represent the best opportunity for achieving a truly proprietary competitive advantage. The advent of transistors provided this kind of opportunity for Texas Instrument, as did the subsequent advent of integrated circuits. A much older example is the silent mercury switch introduced by General Electric, which still has little direct competition. The classical example, of course, is nylon for Du Pont.

The likely trends and trajectories in the conventional technology are fairly evident. The development of a competing technology is a type of mutation that is difficult to anticipate. Certainly the silk growers didn't anticipate nylon! In fact, recognizing its potential utility in a particular application is perhaps the key step in such innovation. As noted earlier, these developments frequently arise even outside the industry, and the originator of the breakthrough may not perceive the breadth of its potential.

Since it is unusual for an organization to develop dedicated enthusiasm for overthrowing its own technical traditions, skillful attention is required to insure that some uncommitted part of the organization is charged with conducting the wide-ranging surveillance needed to uncover potentially competing technologies and to perceive their implications. Needless to say, this continuing competition between alternative technical solutions redounds to the advantage of the consumer through lower costs, greater convenience, reliability, etc.

New Technology Permitting a New Function. The other subset of work in the new technology class involves the development of techniques that make possible a truly new function or product, or which so drastically alter the caliber of man's capability that it constitutes a difference in kind, and not in degree; the heart pacer, television, picture phone, Xerox and Land camera are well-known examples. Events of this type are so rare and unique that they really should be regarded as a separate class. They are the stuff every inventor dreams of and, if successful, they nearly always lead to the creation of a new business or possibly even a new industry. They must be regarded as statistical freaks and as such they fall outside the normal processes of planning and management.

Summary

This spectrum of four classes of technological inputs provides the businessman, as a potential inventor in R&D, with the opportunity to develop a portfolio of technological opportunities (and risks). He can choose a low-risk approach, relying principally on application of state-of-the-art; he can "go for broke" by betting on a speculative new technology; or he can seek a technology portfolio of "balanced" risk. He can even evaluate alternative portfolios, and the generation of viable alternatives is an important feature of strategy formulation, a subject to be taken up in Chapter 8. But first let us review the structure that is beginning to emerge. The earlier discussion of business objectives and alternatives to technology provided a means of describing and evaluating technological objectives in the same terms used for other functions and in language with which the general manager is familiar. The present discussion has examined technological inputs primarily in terms of risk (a familiar concept) and in terms of alternatives that can be weighed and balanced (a familiar process).

A businessman tends to get uncomfortable when somebody talks about how much basic research is, or should be, done in the organization. He lacks the knowledge and background to make such a judgment. Similarly, when one talks about exploratory work, a manager feels defensive about being skeptical, for who can be opposed to the search for a major breakthrough. On the other hand, he finds it exceedingly difficult to make a judgment as to the attractiveness of the area, its potential relevance to his business, and the investment needed to achieve success. Consequently, he cannot determine whether his money is better spent in such exploratory work, or in manufacturing, or in some of the other options that are available to him. Many of the decisions that involve the distribution of resources in technical work must lie within the purview of the director of research and development, and they result from his determination of what is necessary in order to perform the R&D work satisfactorily. He should not ask the leaders of the company to make decisions of this type, nor is it necessarily even very profitable for him to attempt to educate them as to the justification for his decisions. However, he should maintain a continuing dialogue with them within the framework of the technological inputs and outputs we have been discussing.

In Chapter 8 we will be considering the role of technology in business strategy and trying to devise a framework for insuring that potential contributions of technology are adequately incorporated into the formulation of strategic possibilities. We will then consider measures needed to insure that adequate technological inputs will be provided to support the strategy eventually chosen.

8

Formulating the Role of Technology in Business Strategy

We have now developed *two* classes of concepts that can form the basis for formulating the role of technology in business strategy: a spectrum of strategic alternatives and a spectrum of technological inputs. This chapter investigates the formulation of the role of technology in overall business strategy, and Chapter 9 will deal with the formulation of strategy for the R&D organization itself. The discussion of the alternatives to technological innovation in business strategy provided a spectrum of possible strategic alternatives and business objectives (cost, performance, features, etc.), again, presumably, leading to a specific combination of ways for implementing any given strategy. We will find, however, that the formulation of a specific strategic plan involves the consideration of an important additional factor, the competitive situation. Any sound strategic plan must take into account the competitive position of the particular business; it must identify and characterize the major competitors which that business faces; and it must attempt to anticipate the strategies these competitors are likely to follow, including their possible response to any strategic plan established by the business for itself.

To recapitulate the discussion of alternative strategic options for a business, four major strategic possibilities are identified. The first is the maintenance of the status quo, or what might be termed a long-term harvesting mode with respect to a particular business. The second is to grow the business within the context of its present markets and its present technology. Third is to extend the business, building on strengths in marketing and/or technology by going into associated products or associated markets, and finally to diversify the business by seeking to provide new services to society.

Within each of these strategic possibilities the businessman also has a variety of specific business objectives that he may employ to implement a strategy. Presumably, these objectives in one way or another can lead to his acquiring a competitive advantage. They include lower cost, improved performance, the development of new and attractive features, the development of a new level of value added through vertical integration, and finally, the invention of a new function to offer to society to serve a need he perceives—an invention that does not necessarily call for new technology. It is likely that the typical business strategy will involve some mixture of at least the first three, and possibly the fourth element of these specific business objectives, rather than concentrate on a single one.

As we saw earlier, the businessman also has available a spectrum of ways in which to use technology to implement these strategic alternatives and specific objectives. He may apply the present state-of-the-art. He may extend the present state-of-the-art. The discussion above would suggest that with the introduction of the competitive situation as an aspect of strategic planning, he must also give consideration to the technologies being employed by competitors, technologies that may differ significantly from those he utilizes; for example, disc versus drum brakes, gas-cooled nuclear reactors versus water-cooled reactors, welded assemblies versus bolted assemblies. While these competing technologies represent a subset of the present state-of-the-art, they may well be unfamiliar to his organization and therefore their application represents a risk. He may also seek to develop new competing technology to supplant that presently being used. And, finally, he may seek to invent an entirely new function based on new technology, such as Xerography, to serve society.

We come now to the task of putting together these various possibilities into specific combinations that can represent a variety of possible strategies for the business. It should be readily apparent that there is no algorithm with which the strategic planner can develop quick and easy answers to the difficult questions raised in formulating a strategy. There is no substitute for the difficult and painstaking task of trying to raise and evaluate, frequently on a judgmental basis, all relevant questions that should be addressed in arriving at a determination of what is the best combination for his particular business. Let us consider some of these questions for each of the four classifications with which we have been dealing.

Evaluating Strategic Options

The evaluation of the alternative strategic possibilities of harvesting versus growth versus extension versus diversification involves questions that go well beyond the potential contribution of technology. The most important questions concern the projected growth rates of the markets now being served by the business and the relative attractiveness of their future prospects. If a market is presently growing rapidly and gives every indication of continued rapid growth, it is questionable whether a business should divert its managerial, technical, and financial resources to exploit other areas. Conversely, if present market growth rates are relatively unattractive in terms of business goals and the aspirations of management, then the search for more attractive opportunities becomes much more important as an alternative to adopting a harvest strategy for the present business.

The present competitive position must also be evaluated dispassionately. A business that already has a powerful position in its present markets is in a better position to seek additional challenge in nearby areas. On the other hand, a business that is presently struggling for survival and facing severe competitive pressure would be foolish to seek additional challenge. In addition, occasional transitory internal problems may make it unwise for a business to assume additional challenge by entering nearby markets. For example, it would be unwise to initiate a new venture when there is severe labor shortage or unrest, shortage of capacity that must be alleviated, or changes in government regulations that require changes in the modus operandi of the business.

Quite obviously, one must be able to identify attractive associated markets or new products requiring associated markets or new products requiring associated technologies that the business might seek to exploit. Unless such opportunities can be identified and unless the management of the business is suitably equipped to lead the effort of extension or diversification, no true strategic alternative exists. This aspect of strategy formulation offers the greatest opportunity for creativity and vision on the part of planners and executives.

Finally, one must consider the aspirations and competence of the management together with the strength and depth of the human resources of the business. This subject encompasses not only the level of ambition of management with respect to the future growth of the business, but also the breadth of its experience in managing ambitious growth or diversification plans. These questions are absolutely basic because every strategy rests on the fundamentals of the aspirations, competence, and drive of the management. Going further, one must also examine the functional strength of the organization. Does it have at hand in the manufacturing, marketing, and engineering functions the kinds of capabilities that would enable it to take on a significantly larger challenge without sacrificing competitive position in its present markets? For example, it appears that Rolls Royce had inadequate managerial and functional strength to sustain its major thrust into the United States commercial jet-engine market.

Analysis and evaluation of the kinds of questions discussed above provide the basis for choosing the combination of harvest/grow/extend/diversify which seems most appropriate for the specific business. It also sets the stage for the next phase, which is the selection of the combination of specific business objectives that will be used to implement the chosen strategy.

Evaluation of Business Objectives to Implement the Strategy

The questions to be explored in determining the balance among cost, performance, features, and vertical integration can be considered under three broad headings: (1) the characteristics of the market now being served; (2) the current competitive position of the various product lines and the strategies being pursued by competitors; and (3) the state of technology presently or potentially being used in the industry.

Characteristics of the Market

The questions in this area are concerned primarily with the relative value placed on performance versus price in the particular marketplace being addressed by the business. How much value does the customer attach to differences in performance and, just as important, how apparent can differences in performance be made to seem in his eyes? Where differences in performance are very important to the customer and can be clearly established a business obviously must maintain product performance superiority. It must also appraise the price sensitivity of the customer. For the commodity type of product where product differentiation is difficult, small differences in price are crucial and cost leadership must receive high priority. If products can be differentiated through style or features, or if purchases can be related to emotional appeals, then price sensitivity is likely to be less.

Unfortunately, the typical situation will involve elements of all these factors—performance, price, and features—and success will lie in finding the right combination for the particular business. Such a combination will take advantage of particular strengths, avoid head-to-head confrontation with competitors in areas of weakness, and provide a broad enough appeal to customers to create markets large enough to be attractive. The careful delineation of the precise market segment that the business will seek is a crucial input to technical planning because it guides engineering in making design trade-offs. Matching performance and cost with value as perceived by the specific customers being attracted is the key business consideration that must guide technology planning. Maytag, for example, has traditionally aimed for a high performance market that is willing to pay for performance, long life, and reliability. This decision must guide its technical effort. The Du Pont experience with Corfam is an object lesson of a product that was a technical success and which had excellent performance, but which did not have the right balance of performance and cost to give the customer an adequate perceived value in relation to competing materials.

Competitive Position of the Business

While the competitive position of the firm has been evaluated in a general sense in the selection of the overall strategy, it must be evaluated in detail in selecting specific objectives for implementation. What market penetration has it been able to achieve? How strong are its channels of distribution? In what product lines does it have product and/or cost leadership? What is its position with respect to other major competitors in the market? How dynamic is the competitive situation—are major competitors well known and relatively predictable entities or is the market in turmoil, with new competitors appearing? A competitive position in a state of flux (such as exists in urban mass transportation), with new competitors entering the field and new vendor relationships being established, will present a very uncertain and perhaps threatening competitive situation. But its very fluidity presents attractive new opportunities to the swift and resourceful new entrant, opportunities much more attractive than trying to break into an established and stable competitive structure.

Closely related, of course, is the question of the technical strength and the apparent technical strategy of competitors. If one is dealing with strong competitors in performance-sensitive markets, technology must perforce stress product performance. If, on the other hand, the competitors seem to seek only adequate technical performance while stressing low cost and rapid response, the business must appraise the relative advantages of meeting the competition head-to-head on cost compared to seeking product superiority at a price the customer will still find attractive.

In exploring these questions, however, one must again be careful to identify markets with precision. Skillful and imaginative segmentation can make it possible for a business or its competitors to compartmentalize a market in such a way that its particular product finds a special niche, which neatly finesses competition. This segmentation can occur with relatively low visibility and thus need not trigger a major competitive reaction.

Present State of Technology

Evaluation of the significant trends in technology begins with the business itself. Is its technology relatively low on its learning curve and changing rapidly, with considerable opportunity for achieving future competitive advantages? Has this technology already propelled the business to a position of leadership or is the business behind technically? One must also explore the competing technological approaches already being pursued by different competitors seeking to serve the same customers. In a complex industrial society such as ours it is rare for a single technological approach to constitute the sole means of satisfying a customer's need in such areas as fossil fuel versus nuclear energy in power generation, electrical appliances versus gas appliances, synthetic fibers versus natural fibers, and composite plastic furniture versus wood.

What are the apparent advantages and limitations of the various approaches? In what ways are customer desires changing so that some technical approaches may encounter intrinsic limitations before others do? Finally, what is the possibility of a new technology being developed to supplant all or many of those now being used—say, a major materials substitution, a leapfrog advance in automation, or a new design concept such as the tape cassette?

Consideration of these questions in relation to the present state of technology brings the strategic planner to the general subject of the way in which he will seek to bring technology to bear on the business. That is, what kinds of technological inputs will be required to achieve the chosen business objectives?

Evaluating Technological Inputs

The evaluation of the spectrum of possible ways for technology to be brought to bear is anticipated to a considerable extent in the evaluation of specific business objectives for implementing a strategy.

Applying State-of-the-Art

The attractiveness of this type of input is determined by the degree of maturity of the conventional technology and the competitive position of the firm. If the technology has been practiced for a long time, much of it is in all probability widely available to others as well; therefore, seeking a competitive edge by this route is unlikely to be rewarding. Conversely, for a business that has established a powerful competitive position by the use of technology for which it sees continued avenues for advance, proposals to explore alternative approaches are not likely to be attractive. Despite the desire of the technologist to switch to newer, more personally exciting technologies, the strategic planner should quite properly insist that everything possible be done with conventional state-of-the-art technology or extensions thereof. We possess an enormously rich and powerful technical arsenal, and imaginative application of what is already known will continue to provide a rich reward for those who seek it.

Competing Technology

The viability of a strategy emphasizing application of the state-of-the-art also depends on the extent to which competing technology already being used by competitors may offer a better match to future performance requirements. The dilemma of the tire manufacturers in deciding when to switch to radials is a recent example. This evaluation presents a particularly demanding problem because it requires the technologists in a given business to be objective in comparing the technology to which they have already made a commitment with that being applied by others. The likelihood of bias in favor of home-grown technology is exceedingly difficult to counter.

The most difficult aspect of the problem is the need to appraise the relative future advantages of the alternative technologies and the location of each on its respective growth curve. In order to make this comparison, it is necessary to extrapolate the likely future characteristics of customer demand and at the same time to extrapolate the likely future trends in the development of each competing technology, and then to appraise which is most likely to offer the best future competitive advantage in serving the customer.

Extending the State-of-the-Art

Virtually any product design or manufacturing process offers opportunities for improvements that reduce cost or improve performance, and every business should assume that its competitors will make such improvements. Once again, however, the extent to which this change of the state-of-the-art should be emphasized in seeking competitive advantage depends to a considerable degree on the maturity of the technology. Technology that is relatively low on its growth curve will likely advance rapidly and will permit significant increments of progress for effort expended. As the technology matures, however, advances will become asymptotic.

A parallel consideration is the rate of change in customer demands. If they are escalating or changing rapidly, incremental improvements in technology must be larger, and hence entail greater risk. Progress is sometimes interrupted by performance barriers which cannot presently be surmounted or by design assumptions that are no longer valid. The difficulty of Consolidated Edison with its "Big Allis" generator is a classical example of exceeding the permissible regime of the design assumptions. Consequently, it may be desirable to initiate an insurance effort, namely, explore alternate technologies or enlarge the fundamental understanding of the phenomena involved. The effort to control pollution is an excellent example of this situation. Everything possible is being done to meet requirements by improvements and extensions in present technology, but parallel efforts are exploring new approaches and seeking fundamental understanding.

Developing New Technology to Supplant Old

Successful implementation of this approach requires great skill, skill usually acquired by direct participation in the opening up of the technology. This type of opportunity is created either by the invention of a basic new approach to an old function or by the perception of the applicability of an invention made elsewhere. Inventions of this sort typically involve a potential discontinuity in performance and/or cost, with many unknowns to be risked in the initial applications. The identification of pioneering applications in which the unique advantages of the new technology can have greatest leverage may be crucial to its successful introduction. By the same token, advances of this sort frequently represent the best opportunity for achieving a true proprietary advantage. The likely trends and trajectories in the further advance of state-of-the-art technology are fairly evident to any practitioner in the field, but the evolution of a new competing technology represents a type of development whose introduction is difficult to anticipate.

The gradual takeover of solid-state power electronics in conversion and control of electricity is a textbook example of a new technology supplanting an old. The invention of power diodes and silicon-controlled rectifiers provided unparalleled flexibility, stability, precision, and ruggedness. However, in their early classical pattern the devices were expensive, had unproven reliability, came in a limited range of power-handling capability, and were very vulnerable to voltage surges. Their first applications were in fields such as spinning synthetic fibers, where the devices were uniquely suited to provide the precise control of tension needed. These early applications were made by placing the solid-state device developers, both organizationally and physically, close to those designing the control equipment. Applications gradually extended to other areas where unusual control requirements were dominant and the advantages of solid state compensated for the risk. Meanwhile, prices came down, the range of devices broadened, reliability was demonstrated by field experience and engineers in many different industries learned how to cope with the unusual characteristics of the devices that required different design rules. Now these circuits are being applied in consumer products, and their universal use can be confidently expected.

The Strategic Planning Process

The framework we have been developing can be applied to strategy formulation in a sequence of broad steps. At every step in the process the evaluation of internal factors must be accompanied by matching considerations involving market characteristics and trends to the capabilities and strategies of competitors. First is the determination of the total strategy by the optimum mixture of harvesting/growth/extension/diversification. Having chosen the broad strategy mix, it is necessary to specify the combination of business objectives that will be sought in implementing the strategy. Finally, we must select the combination of technology inputs which can best be used to achieve these objectives. Although this process is presented sequentially, it is obviously highly interdependent and requires much iteration.

Exhibit 1 provides a way in which an input/output type of format can be used to approach the problem of determining the basic business strategy. The alternative strategy options and business objectives can be regarded as outputs, while the different ways in which technology can be brought to bear represent inputs. At this early stage specific business objectives should receive little attention. The questions in the left column should be explored in depth before management is in a position to address the kinds of questions suggested in the right column. It is likely that one will wish to explore a variety of combinations before selecting the specific combination to form the chosen strategy. Options A–D suggest schematically the various pos-

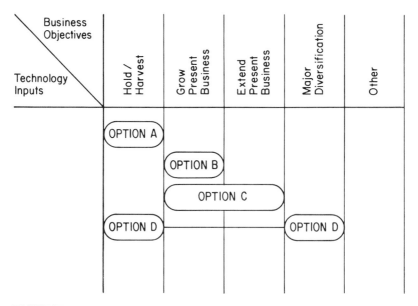

EXHIBIT 1

sibilities a planner might consider with an indication of the relative resources to be applied to various phases of the strategy.

The business options are arranged in order of increasing risk. The most probable sequence is that the planner would first seek to insure that he is doing everything possible to capitalize on the growth opportunities inherent in the present markets. These opportunities must be related to the aspirations of management for the growth of the firm and to the historical rate of growth the business has experienced. Next, he would examine the opportunities for growth by extending the present business into new areas and again compare the projected growth with the aspirations of management. Just as important would be the evaluation of the effort required, and the managerial and functional strength available to divert to the task. If additional growth is still sought or if major opportunities are perceived in remote areas, then the feasibility of undertaking major diversifications should also be explored. Thus, these options need not be regarded as mutually exclusive. Instead, they could be regarded as cumulative, or selectively additive, with increasingly aggressive objectives.

For each strategic combination that seems attractive, one would establish specific goals to be sought in implementing the strategy, and determine the relative emphasis to be placed on each element of the strategy. The specific goals would include tentative growth targets, specific product lines that would generate the growth, and means by which the expansion of the product line sales would be achieved. While the initial consideration of relative emphasis would undoubtedly be qualitative, with terms such as "most" or "major" and "minor" or "subsidiary" being used, the need to introduce allocation of resources would of necessity require increasing quantification. The sequence would perhaps move first to approximate percentages of resources and eventually to approximate dollars of expenditure and proposed areas of effort. These numbers are more expressions of managerial intent at the early stages, but they are needed to inject realism as the plan becomes more specific.

The next broad step in the sequence requires the exploration of alternative combinations of business objectives that could be used to implement the strategies being given serious consideration. Here, once again, the planner must consider specific goals with respect to cost reduction, performance improvement, new features, etc. He must also begin to specify the relative emphasis to be placed on each objective and to estimate the level of resources needed for attainment of each goal. He must then consider the

adequacy of the available resources in relation to the targets established.
And again he must think in terms of sequence on a long-time scale—he is
not planning just for the next year.

Exhibit 2 suggests an input/output format for evaluating these factors.
While one may consider relatively simple strategies such as cost reduction
by extending state-of-the-art, or new features by applying new technology
to supplant old, it is likely that actual strategies will consist of rich mixtures
of a number of elements. In fact, alternative strategies will tend to be
additive, each building on the aggregate of previous alternatives and representing a more aggressive approach. The eventual planning documents
must be much more elaborate and detailed, but the format suggested here
provides a simple way of making preliminary alternative proposals, of

BUSINESS OBJECTIVES / TECHNOLOGY INPUTS	HOLD / HARVEST			GROW PRESENT BUSINESS			EXTEND PRESENT BUSINESS		
	Improved Performance	Improved Cost	New Features	Improved Performance	Improved Cost	New Features	New Level of Value Added	Associated Markets	Associated Technologies
Apply the State-of-the-Art	OPTION A	OPTION B							
Extend the State-of-the-Art								OPTION C	
Competing Technology Used by Others									
New Alternative Technology to Supplant Old					OPTION D				

EXHIBIT 2

comparing the merits of different strategies, and of summarizing both plans and performance for reporting purposes. Again the options suggest schematically different strategies that might be pursued.

Exhibit 3 illustrates in very simplified form a range of hypothetical options that might be considered by an electric motor business. In general, the options would be incremental, with the most conservative being to concentrate on reducing cost simply by applying the state-of-the-art, concentrating on production engineering. Option B would be aimed at improving market share by eliminating a troublesome bearing-failure problem. Option C would propose to extend the business through backward integration by installing a solventless wire-enameling facility so the business could produce its own magnet wire. Option D is the most ambitious: It proposes entering a new market by developing a new linear motor, a technology that

BUSINESS OBJECTIVES / TECHNOLOGY INPUTS	HOLD / HARVEST			GROW PRESENT BUSINESS			EXTEND PRESENT BUSINESS		
	Improved Performance	Improved Cost	New Features	Improved Performance	Improved Cost	New Features	New Level of Value Added	Associated Markets	Associated Technologies
Apply the State-of-the-Art	(A) REDUCE SHOP COST								
Extend the State-of-the-Art				(B) REDESIGN BEARING TO IMPROVE LIFE					
Competing Technology Used by Others							(C) PRODUCE OWN MAGNET WIRE WITH SOLVENT-LESS COATING TECHNIQUE		
New Alternative Technology to Supplant Old							(D) DEVELOP LINEAR MOTOR FOR TOY TRAIN MARKET		

EXHIBIT 3

is different from conventional motors, but which performs the same function, i.e., propulsion.

This format can be also used to characterize the perceived strategy of competitors. The attempt to complete the description of competitive strategies will in itself be a useful exercise. One can assess a competitor's strengths and weaknesses; evaluate his likelihood of success in pursuing his strategy; and then appraise the attractiveness of one's own strategy as a counter to moves by the competition.

Concurrently, specific consideration must also be given to the manner in which technology will be used to achieve the business objectives. This task requires the formulation of specific technical programs to achieve targeted objectives; the appraisal of the need for insurance programs or for parallel efforts where there is considerable uncertainty over the attainability of objectives; the determination of the possible allocation of resources among the various technical programs; and finally the exploration of the manner in which the planned technical inputs will in fact be realized.

This latter step involves appraisal of in-house capabilities, consideration of inputs that can be provided by vendors, and examination of other available external resources. While vendors can be a rich source of "free" technology if properly motivated, it is necessary to the business to have at least some duplicate capability in order to be able to write demanding specifications, evaluate the capability of vendor technical resources, and monitor the performance of vendor products. Additional external resources include licensors, contract R&D organizations, and the purchase of companies possessing valuable technology. Determination of the appropriate course of action in a specific case should be approached with the same type of rationale that is used in arriving at make-buy decisions. Special allowance must be made for the value of proprietary information and for the uncertainty inherent in evaluating the relative costs of developing technology as opposed to purchasing it externally.

Summary

The approach we have been describing emphasizes that technology is not a thing apart but rather is embedded in the very fabric of the business. Many business decisions cannot sensibly be made unless they take into account technological factors, but at the same time many technological decisions cannot be soundly based unless they take into account nontechnical factors in the marketplace, in finance, in management, etc. Strategic options, business objectives, and possible technological inputs must be combined and iterated in different combinations. It is important for technical inputs to be related to business and strategic objectives and not just to some particular product development program, as is frequently the case. That phase comes later, and if R&D enters only at that phase, it's relegating its role to the implementation of strategy. Conversely, R&D cannot meaningfully participate in the formulation of strategy unless it can couch its inputs in terms consistent with the concepts of strategic planning.

9

Strategic Planning for Research and Development

We have now set the stage for considering the subject of strategic planning for research and development. The sequence we have been considering is important because it emphasizes the necessity for strategic planning to be carried out in the context of the total business plan for the corporation. Furthermore, the strategic plan for research and development must make allowance for the culture of the corporation and the organization structure through which its outputs must be generated and fed into the rest of the company. Thus, we have already examined the management climate for innovation, the crucial feature of the culture; we have considered alternative ways in which the strategic options may be executed other than by the use of technology; we have also considered various ways in which technology itself can be brought to bear on achieving strategic business objectives. In Chapter 8 we considered the process by which these various elements could be combined to form a business strategy and a plan of implementation that specified the role of technology.

Selection of Objectives

The kind of planning we discuss in this chapter has rarely been undertaken in American industry, despite the facts that a great deal of attention has been devoted to the subject of planning research and development projects, and that the literature is full of discussions of the use of mathematical models for optimizing program selection. Detailed program planning of the type associated with techniques such as PERT is indeed an indispensable part of the management tools used in running a research and development organization, but by definition this approach is essentially inwardly focused. Its application assumes an unsupported conclusion—that the objective has already been established. The goal of these planning techniques is to increase the efficiency with which objectives are achieved. On the other hand, as we will see, the specification of the objectives is the crucial feature of strategic planning.

Distinction Between Strategic Planning and Project Selection

It is important to distinguish between strategic planning and project selection. The question of how to select projects when funds are limited is, not surprisingly, one of universal interest. So much confusion exists over this subject that it is worth an extended diversion to examine it in some detail. Perhaps the most frequent question that foreigners ask of the management of research and development in this country is, "How do you select projects?" They appear to assume that, given the large amount of money spent on research and development in the United States, we must have developed some magic formula that provides simply and directly the answer to the difficult question of "How should I spend my limited resources?" R&D managers do in fact keep hoping that there is some easier or more certain approach than the judgmental one they are using. They keep hoping that there is some more quantitative approach, which will lend greater certainty or precision to the project selection process.

It is apparent, however, that R&D managers engaged in the real work of project selection have an ambivalent attitude toward these quantitative methods. Their technical tradition tells them that whatever has not been measured is known with great uncertainty, if it is known at all, because a basic principle underlying all technical work is that progress rests on the ability to measure. Consequently, it is not surprising that technical people feel exceedingly uncomfortable with the requirement to rely on nonquantitative methods—they call them "subjective." By that same token, however, it is apparent that they also fear that quantitative methods will be applied indiscriminately by a management which does not appreciate the limitations of such methods. Their reaction to proposals to introduce the use of quantitative techniques is, "I agree in principle that we should use quantitative methods, but you must be very careful. If these techniques are not applied with great wisdom, they will do much more harm than good because they are grossly inadequate. Their application requires the use of detailed and sophisticated judgment, which is available only to those close to the work."

As noted above, a very substantial literature already exists on the creation of rigorous quantitative techniques for program selection, which presumably lead to the optimum use of resources. We must be careful not to regard these techniques as methods of measurement, however. They are better described as precise statements of relationships among quantities, which must be developed by judgment, by estimation, or by projection. These mathematical selection techniques typically assume a set of circumstances in which the following factors are given:

1. The goals of the organization.

2. Some indication or measure of the contribution of each program toward the attainment of these goals; in other words, some sort of performance measurement or criterion for a particular research program that specifies its objectives in operational terms.

3. The risk inherent in carrying out the work.

4. The marginal utility curve expressing the degree of incremental gain or incremental reduction in risk which can be achieved by expending a specified sum of money on a particular program.

With this set of inputs provided for each program to be undertaken by the organization, it is supposedly possible to specify a mathematical process that will optimize the application of available funds among the programs. The only difficulty with this approach is that it requires so many "givens" in order to achieve the solution that the "givens" become the problem.

Presumably, if one had a very large number of programs to include in the allocation process, one might need some sort of mathematical technique or at least numerical methods for keeping track of judgments. For most R&D organizations the principal management concern is over establishing reasonable *judgments* on the quantitative "givens" that the numerical techniques require. Applying rigorous analytical techniques to gross judgmental inputs is very dubious methodology.

The belief that quantitative methods will make the task of R&D program selection easier is undoubtedly illusory anyway. This belief is related to a more general belief widespread in our society, i.e., that the creation of additional knowledge will reduce our areas of uncertainty and eliminate unknowns and thereby will improve the quality of life. We are learning through bitter experience that what it does instead is to bring about major changes in the character of the problem identification, planning, and decision-making process. It makes it possible for us to perceive and to tackle problems of ever larger magnitude and complexity, and to seek levels of precision that heretofore would have been impossible even to consider or perhaps even to comprehend. Thus, increased knowledge and improved manipulative skill simply confront mankind with the anxiety of continuing to deal with newly discovered problems that seem beyond its capability to solve, and compound the difficulty by imposing the requirement to gain mastery over even more sophisticated methodology.

The same situation is to a substantial extent true in the much more limited arena of the management of research and development. Managers believe that more knowledge and better methodologies will create improvement in program selection and thus simplify and ease their task. They will find, however, that these improved methodologies tend to sharpen areas of disagreement among those who participate in the program-planning process because attempts to apply them will focus attention on fundamental differences in values and priorities among the managers. The application of these methodologies will also increase uncertainty by calling attention to new areas of ignorance that exist at higher levels of abstraction and complexity. They will also increase the number of factors taken into account in reaching a decision, simply by creating a capability to take more factors into account. Consequently, decision making may well become more demanding, not less.

Thus, while the search for improved techniques for allocating limited resources among research programs is indeed a valuable exercise to continue, it is important for us to acquire a more realistic understanding of the advantages to be gained and of the problems that the process will itself create. Quantitative and analytical methods do help organize and summarize the available information. They make it possible for R&D managers to take into account a larger range of factors, and they increase the likelihood of achieving optimum allocation by applying traditional standards. Furthermore, these techniques help to clarify relationships among various factors, simply by attempting to state them formally. In this process they bring into sharp focus differing priorities and interpretations of future benefits among the members of the management team and thus they clearly aid in clarifying communication.

Nevertheless, program selection techniques of the type we have been discussing are applicable to the planning that is downstream from strategic planning. They assume that much important spadework has already been done in specifying the goals of the business, the role of technology, and the major technical areas of interest—subjects which are at the heart of strategic planning.

SCOPE OF STRATEGIC PLANNING

Strategic planning addresses itself to two fundamental questions: First, how large should the R&D organization be over the years ahead, i.e., what share of corporate resources should be allocated to this effort? Second, how should its resources be distributed over alternative basic objectives? Only after this broad structure has been established does it make any sense to approach the problem of identifying individual programs that might be undertaken and of determining the optimum level of resources to assign to these programs.

It is necessary to establish first the dimensions within which this planning will be undertaken. These dimensions exist along two axes. The first is the time scale for planning. In strategic planning this time scale must be sufficiently long that essentially all questions are open-ended. In other words, the time scale permits modification of the basic mission of the organization; it permits major changes in the organization, including the people resources; it must even make allowance for the introduction of programs the organization is at present totally unprepared to undertake insofar as the knowledge and skill of its present staff are concerned.

The second dimension might be termed the "interactive horizon" within which planning will occur. By this we mean the couplings to other parts of the corporation, which must provide the inputs needed in R&D and through which the transition of results into commercial use will be achieved. Again, the planning process must permit contemplating changes in any of the constraints under which the organization operates in its coupling relationship. In other words, we are using the largest possible horizon in which to examine the planning of the research and development activity. Only by taking this approach can we provide room to examine all the questions that underline the "givens" which eventually lead—either by a rigorous "quantitative" process or by a judgmental process—to the establishment of a specific set of R&D programs for a specific organization.

Inputs from the Corporate Strategy

Obviously, the determination of the size of the R&D organization or the allocation of its resources over broad objectives cannot be performed independently. The entire planning process is an iterative one, which for purposes of presentation we must treat sequentially. As our earlier discussion indicated, before this planning process can be undertaken the R&D organization must receive some inputs about, or must make some basic assumptions about, the future of the corporation itself. In particular, it must know the extent to which the corporation expects to achieve its growth objectives by capitalizing on the growth dynamics of the markets in which it is now functioning, by extending itself into associated markets and technologies building on its strengths, or by diversifying into major new areas from its present modes of operation. Even more important, the R&D organization needs to know the relative emphasis to be placed on technology and the kinds of technological inputs to be used in implementing the strategy.

This decision involves principally a choice between using technology as a principal thrust for business success, i.e., relying on technological leadership as a major competitive weapon versus choosing to deemphasize technology and stress other aspects of the business. Traditionally, companies and even nations have chosen one or the other of these modes of operation in applying technology. And the record clearly demonstrates that either can be applied with great success. In virtually every sector of the American economy—e.g., electronic, electrical, chemical, pharmaceutical, communications—one can find impressive examples of companies that have grown and prospered through pioneering application of technology. Similarly, one can find companies that have been exceedingly successful in both growth and profitability by adopting a follower position with respect to technology.

Nevertheless, either by acquiring inputs from the corporate management or by making assumptions, the strategic planning process for R&D must begin by specifying the strategy and business objectives of the total organization and the role of technology in achieving them. Against this backdrop the R&D component must first reach agreement with corporate management with regard to the manner in which it will support the corporate objectives, i.e., its mission as specified by corporate management. An operational statement of the mission fundamentally resolves into the question of how much of its effort will be devoted to supporting, monitoring, and defending the present businesses of the company versus the effort devoted to creating opportunities for and/or supporting extension or diversification. In principle, one should perhaps make this decision a priori, but in practice it evolves from an examination of the needs and opportunities that emerge in analyzing the various technical areas of importance to the company and the work already under way in the laboratory.

What *is* important to establish from the beginning is the relative priority to be placed on supporting present business versus supporting extension and diversification as each technical area is analyzed. The public perception of R&D would place higher priority on the latter; in practice, most R&D effort reflects a higher priority on the former. These priorities should be established at least tentatively in consultation with corporate management before strategic planning is initiated. Only then is it possible to address the two questions of how large the R&D organization should be and how its resources should be allocated among major objectives.

DETERMINING THE SIZE OF THE R&D EFFORT

The problem of determining the projected size of the research and development organization is one of universal interest. Methodologies for making these determinations appear to be in a primitive state. In principle, the size should be determined by deciding how much effort is required to achieve the technology inputs necessary to implement the chosen corporate strategy. In practice, this determination cannot be made with sufficient precision to be credible. Consequently, the process is in fact partly a political one involving the balancing of power among all functions and partly an extrapolation of corporate management's feeling of satisfaction with past contributions from R&D. This discussion will focus on the distinction between the actual as opposed to the apparent factors that are involved in the process. It will also suggest some additional considerations for testing and experimentation in future work in this area.

The most commonly used technique is an extrapolation of trends, typically based on three kinds of data combined with a "sales pitch" for the great

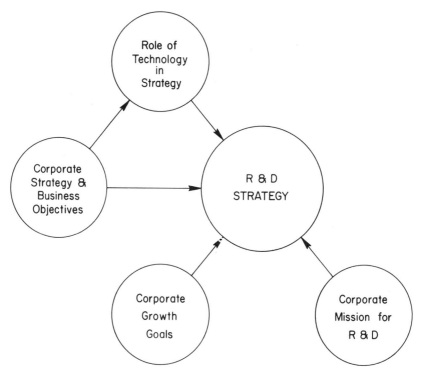

FIG. 9.1

things that would result from additional expenditures for R&D. The trend data include the growth rate and the absolute magnitude of the dollars expended on research and development, the relationship of R&D expenditures to sales, and a comparison with the industry in which one is competing. This process begins by comparing the traditional level of expenditures for R&D with sales, then uses the sales forecast of the company to extrapolate a growth rate for research and development, and then compares this rate of growth with the traditional rate of growth in the R&D function. Finally, both latter quantities are sometimes compared with the trends of growth in the industry as a whole to see whether the projections would lead to any change in past relationships with the industry.

Unfortunately, the principal advantage of this technique is that it does involve calculations that are possible to make. Corporate management quite naturally asks: "Why should there be any necessary relationship between R&D expenditures and sales? Aren't there economies of scale which you people in R&D should be able to realize as the organization grows, or is it necessary to spend an incremental amount of money on research and development for every additional dollar of sales?" Nevertheless, comparison with sales is the most widely used criterion. Probably the most cogent argument for the use of this criterion is the comparison with competition. Each major segment of industry—electronics, chemicals, pharmaceuticals, electrical equipment, etc.—tends to generate a characteristic level of R&D expenditures, and while no individual company need match this level, it does represent a valid baseline against which to compare expenditures.

The effort to sell additional R&D effort is undoubtedly necessary, for the senior executives of major companies spend their lives listening to special pleaders seeking additional resources. These executives see as one of their principal responsibilities the allocation of limited resources, and this requires them to say "no" frequently. Consequently, they represent a very tough audience from which to extract additional support. Their faith in R&D will rest largely on their judgment of how effective and responsive the R&D component has been in the recent past.

The actual process of determining R&D expenditures is in fact very much a political one, which is perhaps best described as an adversary process. The manager of research and development, as an advocate of his function, not suprisingly would like his organization to grow because he is convinced of the value of R&D contributions to the business. Thus, he must attempt to balance two opposing considerations.

First, he would like to ask for as much money as he possibly can hope to receive. He wants to avoid underbidding; otherwise, he has not performed his function well. And furthermore, he may be regarded by corporate management as a relatively weak reed, easily pushed aside in the intricate, relentless maneuvering involved in resource allocation throughout the company. Moreover, in times of stringency R&D expenditures can always be cut to improve current profitability without discernibly impairing the future. The transactions involved in all resource allocation are to a substantial extent an adversary process in which the amount of resistance an individual can generate, and his potential for counterattack and subversion, has a bearing on how well he will be treated in the initial allocation of resources.

Second, the R&D manager wants to avoid having any substantial reduction made in his request for funds. If he asks for too much, he may come to be regarded as unrealistic and insufficiently tuned to the realities of the current business situation. Above everything else, corporate executives want to feel that the people with whom they are dealing understand *their* problems. In navigating between these shoals, the R&D manager tries to keep closely attuned to the apparent climate in the corporate structure. He wants to be aware of the current degree of optimism with which the future is regarded, the sorts of risks and uncertainties which corporate management sees on the horizon in all areas of operation. Of course he also must assess the current status of the R&D organization in the eyes of the management.

Despite all attempts at quantification, this process of determining the amount of resources to be devoted to research and development will inevitably remain a judgmental one. When reduced to essentials it must reflect the values and attitudes and priorities of the chief executive. But it is important for the R&D manager to present the chief executive with as much relevant information as possible to help him gain insights into relationships of R&D effort to other aspects of the business and to perceive the consequences of changes in expenditure in as many meaningful ways as possible. Given this requirement, the traditional mode of relating R&D expenditures to sales is inadequate.

One new approach some have advocated[62] is to assert that R&D expenditures, since they are clearly an investment, will be more meaningful if they are tracked with other investment expenditures for the corporation. The weakness in this approach is that much investment expenditure clearly has no bearing on the need for research and development. By definition, additional plant capacity must be based on state-of-the-art technology. Furthermore, additions to capacity are intrinsically intermittent in nature, and R&D expenditure should clearly avoid following these peaks and valleys.

Perhaps it is more meaningful to relate research and development expenditures to cash flow. Research and development, by virtue of its long-range nature, can be regarded as a type of discretionary expenditure, and cash flow can be considered analogous to discretionary income. Realistic comparison of one with the other may be a better measurement of past management decisions with respect to investment in research and development than would be its relation to sales. Unfortunately, this technique does not lend itself well to competitive comparison because cash flow data by sectors of industry are not presently available, and changes would have to be made in government statistical reporting systems before such data could be accumulated. Until some preliminary studies are made for individual companies, we will not know what relationship (if any) exists between cash flow and R&D expenditures.

Another technique that warrants careful evaluation is to relate R&D expense to *all* expenditures for the growth and improvement of the company. Since we have been arguing that R&D is only a part of the total innovative process and that it should be managed in the context of this total process, it follows that R&D expenditures should be examined in this same context. Analysts who attempt to relate R&D expenditures directly to profitability do R&D a disservice because corporate R&D outputs cannot come to fruition without additional balanced expenditures downstream. These expenditures typically involve capital investment, but they also involve developing manufacturing methods and training workers, market development, building distribution systems, training sales and service personnel, building inventory—a long list, which in total dwarfs the R&D investment. In the aggregate all these factors reflect the total commitment of the management to investing in the future.

Again, little work has been done in this area, and in fact the relevant data quite probably aren't accumulated in many company accounting systems. An effort should be made to accumulate those expenditures that are defined as having as their objective the future benefits to the business rather than the accomplishment of the work necessary to meet this year's operating needs, and to compare research and development expenditures with these sums.

An economist once commented to me that he couldn't understand the penchant of R&D managers for trying to justify their function by treating it as an isolated and independent variable and looking for changes in profitability as a function of changes in level of R&D. "No other function behaves this way," he noted. Other functions increasingly measure performance in terms of accomplishment of objectives in the context of the business plan. The discussion earlier in this book and in this chapter is intended to provide the conceptual framework for R&D to begin to behave in a similar fashion.

While the desired expenditures on R&D must still be established by management judgment, I believe that the portrayal of these additional relationships will provide a more meaningful tool for the businessman to use in applying his judgment. Quantitative methods that attempt to supplant judgment are just as suspect in this case as in the case of project selection discussed earlier in this chapter.

Resource Allocation

The process of allocating resources among alternative objectives begins with arranging for the necessary inputs of information. If R&D planning is to be successful, it must involve the participation of diverse elements from many different parts of the business. The key to this participation will be the ease with which communication can be established. The planning process must make it easy for these diverse elements to contribute inputs in their own language. At the same time it must lead to outputs expressed in terms that seem familiar to the businessmen who use them. Thus, the development of a classification system that will provide a common taxonomy for communication is a crucial ingredient in an effective R&D plan. The classification system may be structured by discipline, by product, by elements of the production process, by market, or by industry. It must in the end represent a system that permits one to deal meaningfully with the question of resource allocation. Furthermore, it must permit the integration of the R&D plan into the total corporate plan. We too often forget that planning tools not only serve internal purposes, but also must aid in communication outside the R&D component. Thus, if at all possible, the work classification system should be output oriented. The familiar classification of basic research, applied research, and development does not fit these criteria. The terms may have some value inside the R&D organization, but they are not helpful to the businessman.

The classification system must permit the R&D organization to address the entire spectrum of technical work it may have to perform in order to fulfill its mission and to divide up this spectrum into areas of interest which are manageable segments. It forms the language by which R&D management discusses its own planning and operation. It also becomes the language into which the inputs from operations are translated in order to be incorporated into the resource allocation and program planning process, and is the language used by R&D to report its plan and accomplishments to corporate management.

I cannot emphasize too strongly the importance of this classificatory language or the difficulty in developing it. It must represent a hierarchical system that begins at the level of the work performed by individual scientists and engineers. From this totally *technical* point of view it must move to higher levels of aggregation that have utility in planning but that continue to appear sensible to technical practitioners. A system that simply provides some convenient bins into which programs can be tossed after the planning is completed is failing its purposes of stimulating and guiding planning as well as serving as a cross check on the comprehensiveness of the effort. At the same time, the classification system at higher levels of aggregation must transform the work into output-oriented terms whose import is understandable to corporate management. It must also represent aggregates whose internal coherence facilitates resource allocation. One of the principal purposes of the hierarchical language must be to group related work so that better decisions can be made regarding the appropriate level of effort.

Needless to say, this language must be developed internally with the direct involvement of the managers who must make it work. The process of development will be slow and frustrating, but it is an indispensable part of planning methodology.

The next step in the planning process is to arrange for the generation of inputs. The objective of this process should be to identify the available options that should be weighed in establishing the plan and to delineate their strengths and weaknesses. It is important to insure that each option is presented with sufficient vigor and clarity to command appropriate consideration. Effective planning is perhaps best regarded as an adversary process. The confrontation among advocates for each position is more likely to elicit the strengths and weaknesses of each. The participants in this adversary process should include the management of the R&D activity itself, the technical staff of the laboratory, the management of operations, corporate management, and corporate staff.

The basic purpose of the inputs is to provide the foundation for establishing the technical objectives that will be pursued in R&D and then to determine the distribution of R&D resources among the various areas of potential interest. We have already described the two main streams of these inputs: supply-push, arising from the creative ideas of the technical staff and the internal dynamics of science and technology; and demand-induced, arising from the perceived needs and opportunities of the business. This latter information can be generated by the management and staff of the laboratory as they look at the business of the company, but it should also be generated by operations themselves; otherwise, the adversary process will probably be out of balance.

The R&D organization should not make the mistake of assuming that it can adequately generate all opposing points of view from its in-house resources. Furthermore, unless operating components are made active participants in the planning process by being asked to generate inputs, they will have no sense of commitment to utilize results as they are produced in the laboratory. Consequently, the R&D plan should include inputs from operations, provided in a specific and formal manner with an indication of the relative priority attached to the principal needs and opportunities identified. The discipline imposed on operations in trying to establish its high priority needs will be a valuable ancillary benefit, as will be the improved communications arising from the dialogue stimulated in transmitting the inputs.

It is also necessary to obtain inputs from the corporate level. For the corporate futurists who are weighing the future character and direction of growth for the entire company, this process should be an interactive one because the R&D plan should also provide an input to the planners as they consider alternative courses for the future of the company. Concurrently, the R&D plan should take into consideration new opportunities that are being evaluated at the corporate level and should analyze the role of technology in pursuing those opportunities. In particular, the R&D plan must take into account the balance evolving in corporate planning between the growth of the company as it now exists and the need to modify the company in order to move into new directions. The accompanying diagram suggests schematically the flow of inputs into R&D planning.

Integrating the Inputs into a Coherent Forecast

The various inputs involving the identification of future needs and opportunities, whether from the internal dynamics of science or from the various perspectives on the likely future course of the business, must be translated into whatever classification scheme has been established. Then these disparate inputs must be synthesized into a coherent picture for each technical output category included in the R&D plan. This activity can be undertaken by a single individual, but it is best done by a technology appraisal team comprising not only people in the staff planning function but also those in the line management of the laboratory.

Input synthesis is in effect a type of technological forecasting. The R&D organization must arrive at some sort of consensus as to the likely future course of events in research and development. This technological forecast

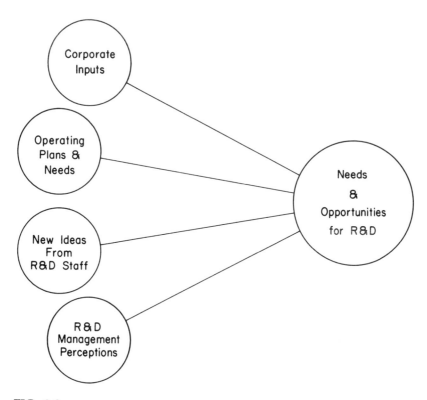

FIG. 9.2

should go beyond the simple prediction of the probability of occurrence of certain events and their timing; it should include the analysis of the implications of these events for the R&D organization and for the company. The forecast should identify the critical driving forces that are instrumental in shaping the future course of events, should specify the advances that these driving forces will generate, and it should identify and evaluate the implications of those events for the individual company. The objective of the forecast, and the criterion by which it should be judged, is to create the basis for identifying and placing in proper priority the long-range technical programs to be undertaken by R&D.

The driving forces should also include factors not technologically based, such as economics, political influences, and changes in societal trends. For example, it is apparent that the driving forces produced by growing concern

with the environment and with the quality of life are critical factors
influencing the likely future course of technology, and they must be taken
into account in the evaluation of opportunities and needs in research and
development. While it is clear that this technological forecast is a frail and
fallible report, it does provide a valuable reference point for one to identify
departures from the predicted direction and to evaluate the impact of these
variations on the R&D plan.

The resulting report will be less detailed and less pretentious than many
technological forecasts that focus on delineating the probability of occurrence and the likely timing of a vast array of discrete events. To be useful in
strategic planning, a scenario of the future must demonstrate coherence,
identify interdependence of factors, and delineate key trends. This approach identifies the broad areas in which more detailed and more limited
analyses may then be found desirable.

As the accompanying schematic of the input synthesis suggests, scenario
forecasts serve to organize and synthesize a large body of inputs regarding

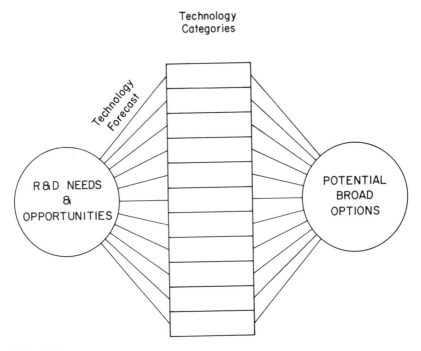

FIG. 9.3

possible R&D needs and opportunities. The technical categories of the classification system provide the structure for organizing the scenarios. The objective of the exercise—to identify broad options for R&D—must always be kept in mind.

Determining Relative Priorities

The technological forecasts for each category identified in the classification system can be used to establish the summary of potential objectives that should be pursued in research and development. But hopefully, the cost of achieving these objectives will be greater than the resources of the organization permit. There are clearly cases in which organizations are idea limited, but that is not the problem we are addressing at the moment. Means must be devised to allocate the limited resources available among the various possibilities, i.e., the establishment of relative priorities. These priorities clearly should reflect some measure of the potential leverage of a technical success if it could be achieved.

We are now approaching the project selection process referred to earlier in the chapter. However, the level at which we are approaching the problem is not that of selecting individual projects, but rather of identifying the relative attractiveness of various broad areas of effort for which resources should be provided in the future course of the laboratory. For example, in today's climate many R&D organizations may well have a technical category associated with environmental problems. Within this category, possible broad areas of investigation could include such problems as meeting plant effluent and emission standards, eliminating toxicity and safety hazards of products, and anticipating end-of-life disposal. Concurrent with identification of these problems there could be opportunities in new monitoring equipment, new ecologically compatible products, or new recycling techniques. The identification and evaluation of individual problems within these areas is a subsequent step in screening out low-priority R&D projects. At this level it is inappropriate to attempt to apply a cost/benefit analysis. Not only are inadequate data available to permit such an analysis on a meaningful basis, but also at this early stage one cannot meaningfully discuss the "costs" of individual projects. The relative effort put into individual projects can be determined only after basic decisions have been made with respect to the long-range distribution of effort among major areas, as the accompanying diagram shows.

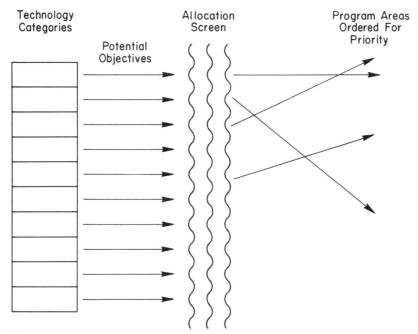

FIG. 9.4

Intuitively, one might feel that the priorities should reflect a combination of two things: One is the potential leverage of technical success on the business, if it can be achieved, and the other is the likelihood of achieving success. This latter factor reflects the magnitude of the technological achievements sought in the program: Is a major and implausible invention needed, or will incremental advances along known paths suffice? It also should reflect the relative promise associated with alternative approaches to this same objective and whether the approach being pursued locally is a front runner or a dark horse. Finally, it should reflect the extent to which the capability of the particular R&D organization is well matched with the technical requirements of the problem. It is apparent that these considerations are somewhat more relevant to the evaluation of individual projects than to total areas. In the extended time frame of strategic planning, many of these factors can be influenced by local management through its choice of specific projects and its manipulation of resources. Nevertheless, an analysis of the likelihood of success can help characterize the time frame required to achieve success and thus influence the implementation plans that are made.

The key feature of the resource allocation process should be the development of some measure of the potential leverage of work in each technical category and the broad areas within a category. It is tempting to provide a simple algorithm for evaluating leverage and to say: "Here is the method you use in establishing relative priorities." But such a step would be doing the reader a disservice. If an analysis of this type is to be used effectively, the methodology *must* be developed locally. It must reflect local management's perception of needs and priorities.

It is interesting to note that many of the factors are not strictly technological in nature, but are the kinds the businessman would take into account in evaluating almost any business alternative. He is always interested in the size of the potential market because it represents the limiting parameter of the success the business can hope to achieve. He is perhaps even more interested in the rate of growth because rapidly growing markets are much more likely to present major opportunities for profitable participation. They also represent situations in which the competitive structure of the industry is likely to be more fluid and in which additional market penetration can be achieved without generating the severe retaliatory reaction that is likely in stable markets.

After having considered the size of the market likely to be impacted by the technical program and its projected rate of growth, one is next interested in the degree of market penetration the company can reasonably expect to achieve. The likely share the company can hope to obtain reflects a combination of two considerations which are also relevant in nontechnical evaluations. One is the total resources that the company chooses, and is able, to bring to bear in establishing market position; the other is the structure of the industry. If powerful, well-entrenched competitors are already in place, obtaining a greater share of the market is likely to be difficult and expensive. If the market is just forming (or has to be created) or if no clear-cut competitive lineup has yet been established, or if the company already has a powerful and effective apparatus serving that market, then obtaining an attractive market share is more likely.

Of course, if a distinctive and economically attractive technological advantage can be established, the constraints on market penetration will have less force. Thus, we come to the technological considerations that affect leverage: What is the sensitivity of the market to technological advance and to what extent is the organization in a position to attack key rate-limiting aspects of the technology as opposed to peripheral or subsidiary issues? As we have noted before, many markets are sensitive to factors, such as style and features, on which technology can have only limited effect. Others, such as communications equipment or data processing equipment, are exceedingly sensitive to product performance, and technological advance is the principal avenue to increased customer satisfaction. In assessing technical impact it is vitally important to establish safeguards for defining markets so that managers cannot exaggerate the potential of their work. For example, office copier equipment requires special light sources. However a manager carrying out R&D on lamps would be deluding himself and others if he asserted that improved lamp sources would significantly affect the rate of growth on the entire office copier market and that his program should be credited with having an impact on that huge market. The dilemma can be resolved in one of two ways. He can be permitted to retain the huge copier market as the target, but then must identify his work as addressing only a subsidiary technology *or* he can identify the *very* much smaller market for copying lamps as the target and then assert that his program is aimed at key technical problems whose solution *would* significantly affect the market.

In developing the algorithms used to evaluate the potential leverage resulting from effort applied to different categories in the classification scheme, a scale must be established for each of the factors discussed above. The number of steps in the scale and the weightings must be determined by local needs and desires. The steps may be arithmetic or logarithmic and the factors may be combined additively or multiplicatively. The indispensable consideration is that each management must develop algorithmic rules that appeal to it as reasonable and practicable. The entire process is strikingly similar to the methodology of constructing a scheme for position evaluation. It is important, however, for the system to provide flexibility and to avoid seeking a degree of precision greater than that which the data would warrant. The temptation to overengineer evaluative systems of this sort must be sternly resisted because the results will not warrant a complex process. Too much sophistication will kill the system.

It is necessary to realize that this evaluation of potential leverage provides only a relative ordering that permits management to create a preliminary listing of technical categories in approximate order of likely impact on the business. This preliminary ordering provides the basis for making additional intuitive judgments. For example, it is apparent that in any actual allocation of resources, attention must be given to the need to concentrate effort. Some fields should probably be eliminated from consideration, simply because they dilute effort and spread it so thin that effective progress cannot be made even in those areas selected for attention. Consideration must also be given to the worth of the ongoing programs being carried out in the laboratory. These programs represent a significant investment in time, money, and manpower. Care must be taken to insure that the potential of this investment is realized before effort is terminated or redirected.

Perhaps the chief value of an evaluation scheme of this sort is to help managers become more aware of the factors they use in making intuitive judgments. Running through this evaluation exercise can help expose management prejudices and help call attention to soft spots in management judgment. In other words, it helps raise the right questions even if it doesn't provide all the answers. Even more important, it provides a structure for discussion and evaluation, which helps to pinpoint sources of disagreement, to clarify areas of controversy, and to identify subjects where more data are needed.

The determination of the absolute level of resources can be approached sequentially. The values derived from the appraisal of leverage establish rough guidelines to the *relative* value of different areas. These must be examined by management in the light of ongoing programs that must be completed, short-term economic factors, and the likely size of the budget. The strategic planning process should serve principally to establish long-term guidelines for changes in resource allocation, i.e., selection of areas to receive increased attention and those to receive diminished effort.

FURTHER STEPS IN IMPLEMENTING THE PLAN

The aspects of strategic planning which remain after this basic and crucial task of resource allocation has been completed have to do principally with considering the implications involved in implementing the strategic plan. They can be classified into three principal groupings. The first is the kinds of resources needed to accomplish the plan. To the extent that the plan involves taking the laboratory into new directions requiring the acquisition of new skills, careful examination will be required of the current mix of people and abilities within the organization and plans made for the necessary adjustments in manpower. A shift may be required in the specific disciplines the laboratory will need to employ, such as a move from the

physical sciences into the life sciences or perhaps into the social or be-
havioral sciences.

Second, a different kind of shift may be required to match a change in the
output the laboratory will be attempting to produce. If the output of the
laboratory is principally associated with supplying pieces of technology for
use by others, its skills will be concentrated on materials, devices, processes, and components. If its output is to be the creation of something that
approaches a system or a major component of a system, it will need quite
different skills and quite probably a different organization structure and
type of management as well. A laboratory whose outputs are principally
materials, devices, and components may very well find it preferable to
organize itself along disciplinary lines. On the other hand, a laboratory
whose output is principally systems or major components of systems may
find it necessary to organize itself along project lines.

Third, any significant change in the long-range strategy of the organization will call for reexamination of the nature of its coupling relationships
with its clients. Here again, the most significant change to keep in mind is
any shift from materials, devices, and components to a systems output. In
the former case, the output of the laboratory is likely to come in relatively
small increments and to be received by technical specialists in operations,
who will incorporate the new technology into products that they themselves are responsible for designing and manufacturing. In the case of a
systems output the results of laboratory effort will emerge as relatively large
increments that are in themselves inherently closer to commercial realization. In this case it is likely that a significant movement of people may be
required to accompany the project as it goes into operations. Furthermore,
care must be taken well in advance of the actual transition to lay the
pathway into the operating department that receives the product because
the size of the undertaking will effect a significant disruption of activities in
the systems component that is to complete the process of commercialization. In fact, outputs of this sort in many cases lead to the creation of a new
commercial organization to exploit the technological advance.

As noted at the beginning of this chapter, the process described here in
sequential fashion is actually an interactive one, and its execution should
lead to an input that will be valued by the corporate planning activity as it
considers long-range objectives for the corporation as a whole. This, in
turn, should feed back into the strategic planning process of the corporate
laboratory so that the eventual R&D plan represents a convergence of the

long-range technical objectives of the corporation and the long-range work of the laboratory. The laboratory planning should have resulted in careful and sophisticated consideration of technological opportunities in the generation of the corporate plan, and the corporate planning should have led to a more realistic appraisal of market opportunities and financial requirements in the development of the corporate R&D plan.

Summary

We have now completed an extended treatment of the interaction between technology and corporate strategy, and the development of R&D strategy in such a way that it both contributes and is responsive to corporate strategy. The focus has been on the process involved rather than on the substantive content or even specific techniques of planning.

R&D strategy must address two key questions: "What resources should be devoted to R&D?" and "How should R&D resources be allocated among alternative uses?" The question of the size of R&D cannot yet be answered by a direct application of marginal utility analysis because we cannot measure output adequately. Consequently, we must fall back on a variety of comparative analyses, comparisons with past levels of effort and with R&D effort of competition. Fundamentally, the R&D budget emerges from an adversary relationship between corporate management and the R&D director.

The allocation of R&D effort must begin with the specification of the mission for R&D. This mission establishes the relative priority to be assigned to work in support of present businesses versus work aimed at creating new businesses.

Planning must then address the formulation of a language that serves the dual needs of facilitating communication within R&D—communication that will be technically oriented—and of communicating with sponsors or customers. Effective planning also requires extensive "homework" in the form of inputs on technology, corporate strategy, operating plans, and significant external forces. These inputs must be obtained from diverse sources, and the R&D component must take care not to synthesize an entirely in-house input which is presumed to represent an adequate statement of the views of others.

From this homework a coherent, integrated statement of key technical needs and opportunities should be prepared, together with an analysis of the implications of these opportunities for the company. This scenario approach can identify targets of potential opportunity that warrant more extended analysis.

Sophisticated, quantitative program selection techniques are not applicable to the broad look we are now taking. Screening procedures that do raise questions about the leverage that technical success would have on the business are needed, however. Likely market impact is the key factor to explore. The strategic planning process is completed by considering the changes in resources, organization, and coupling relationships with the rest of the company needed to implement the plan.

Rather than pursue this process, which will become increasingly concentrated on internal activities within R&D, I propose to return to the primary focus of this book, the interface between R&D and the rest of the organization. First to be considered are some of the specific problems of locating R&D in the organization (Chapter 10). Then we will examine the key topic of the transition of R&D outputs to commercial application (Chapter 11). Chapters 12 and 13 are devoted to the complexities of technical communication in a large company. Chapters 14 and 15 consider some of the special people-focussed problems of managing R&D. Finally, Chapters 16 and 17 attempt to take a look into the future and identify some of the topics which receive increasing managerial attention.

10

Organization of R&D

An examination of the organization of R&D can be approached from two different points of view. One is internal in its focus and is concerned with the organization of the research and development activity itself. This way of approaching the subject receives the most attention. The other approach considers the organization of the R&D activity as a part of the total enterprise and takes into account the organizational requirements associated with producing the different kinds of technical inputs discussed in Chapter 7—application of state-of-the-art, extension of state-of-the-art, and generation of new technology. This approach, which has on the whole received relatively little attention, focuses on two important and relatively unexplored topics, status and coupling. These two topics, as we will see, are incompatible.

First is status. The status accorded the R&D organization by the rest of the company will strongly affect the influence it will be able to exert, and status is strongly influenced by the reporting level of R&D. Second is coupling, the key ingredient in program formulation and the transition of laboratory outputs to commercial application. The nature of the coupling established between the research and development component and the rest of the organization is also strongly influenced by the nature of its reporting relationship.

Centralization vs. Decentralization

For a company large enough to engage in multisite, multiproduct line operations, the question of R&D organization reduces fundamentally to centralization versus decentralization. Should the organization choose to have one research and development component reporting at a reasonably high level in the company—let us say, to the president or some senior executive? Or, should it choose to put research and development close to operations, both organizationally and physically, and perhaps have several research and development organizations associated with different plants or different product lines or different regions of the country? In the first case the R&D function would constitute an organization of some considerable size, with the scope of the entire company within its purview. In the second case each laboratory would presumably be smaller in size and have a smaller scope.

It is quite apparent that the mode of organization for R&D must be related to the role assigned to technology as a part of the total corporate strategy. As we will see, the environmental and reporting relationships that are mandatory for effective pursuit of new technology are quite different from those suitable for applying or extending the state-of-the-art.

As one looks at major corporations in the United States, one can see a spectrum of research and development operations, from complete centralization to complete decentralization. At the most highly centralized end among the large companies is Bell Telephone Laboratories, which performs *all* the technical work on research, advance development, design, and systems engineering for the equipment used in AT&T subsidiary operating companies. Despite its giant size the Bell System is unique in the systems coherence of its operation, and its Bell Telephone Laboratories are unique in the scope and degree of centralization of their charter.

Very close behind in this category are the oil companies, which typically have one or perhaps two corporate subsidiaries that perform all research and development for a corporation. It is not unusual to see the petroleum production R&D—which involves physics, geology, and geophysics —incorporated into a separate organization from that associated with refinery R&D. If the company is heavily involved in petrochemicals, R&D for that particular activity may be organized separately. This same pattern of centralization is found in the drug industry.

At the next level of decentralization we find greater variety. One well-known approach is to combine organizational decentralization with geo-graphical centralization. The Experiment Station of the Du Pont Company is an outstanding example of providing at one site a location for all major laboratories of the various Du Pont departments as well as for the corporate laboratory.

Another approach is to define all *research* as a corporate function, irrespective of where it is performed, and to decentralize *development* by assigning it to the appropriate operating component. Under this arrangement one senior executive would have line responsibility for all research performed in the corporation. IBM and the Philips Company in Holland are well-known examples of this approach. This delineation of research *and* development suggests a clearer dichotomy between the two than actually exists. In practice, a willingness to accept a certain imprecision in the interface and not insist on rigorously pure distinctions seems to mitigate difficulties.

A different approach to decentralization is taken by companies such as General Electric, Westinghouse, and Sarnoff Laboratories of RCA. In these companies there is a physically centralized corporate laboratory that performs a mixture of research and development, but in addition there are very substantial advanced technical activities performed in many of the major business functions of the corporation. These latter activities are both organizationally and geographically decentralized. The interface that exists between this type of corporate laboratory and operations is a varying one; it depends on history, geography, the extent to which technology has an impact on a particular business, the technical strength that exists in the operating departments, and other similar factors. The interface is typically the result of pragmatic accommodation and improvisation rather than careful design.

At still a greater level of organizational decentralization one can find corporate laboratories—the Central Research Department at Du Pont and the Tarrytown laboratories of Union Carbide are excellent examples —which perform research and develop the basis for new business, but which have limited coupling with the operation of present businesses. In these cases the operating components are virtually autonomous technically, and they must contain the internal technical resources to supply their needs.

There are some examples—General Dynamics in this country and ICI in Great Britain are well known—in which all technical work for the corporation is performed on a decentralized basis. Each operating group is self-sufficient technically in all its R&D needs, both with respect to management and the performance of research, but there is a small corporate staff R&D function that attempts to provide coordination and review for the central corporate management. Clearly, in these cases corporate management is looking to operations to provide the entire forward technical thrust for the company.

The final stage of decentralization is one in which all technical work is performed on a decentralized basis and there is no corporate R&D staff function. The new conglomerates tend toward this type of operation; Litton Industries and Colt Industries are typical examples. Companies of this sort put a strong emphasis on financial management and general review of operations without attempting to provide any central corporate services for the enterprise as a whole.

Centralized Laboratories

Both decentralization and centralization have advantages and disadvantages, and the appropriate choice will undoubtedly depend on local circumstances in the individual company. With a centralized organization of R&D—one as large as the total company can support—the advantages are related primarily to larger scope and to detachment from present technology. For example, a large organization is more likely to be able to hire first-rate people who are attracted to the broader scope and greater diversity that it can provide. The technical staff will undoubtedly become more specialized, simply because the scope of problems, the size of the tasks undertaken, and the size of the technical staff itself permit a higher degree of specialization than is possible in a small organization, where people must necessarily become versatile. The continuity with which work can be pursued will also be greater. There is less of breaking off and doing fire-fighting work or moving rapidly from one area to another, first because the centralized lab is better insulated from daily crises and second because its greater size and versatility give it more freedom in protecting the continuity of work at crucial stages.

The equipment used in the centralized R&D component can also be specialized. For instance, a large laboratory typically is able to purchase electron microscopes or mass spectrometers and similar equipment of a sort that a small laboratory couldn't afford because its volume of work would not economically justify acquisition of the equipment. In addition, the size and variety of services and skills available in a larger corporate laboratory give it a flexibility and versatility in mobilizing resources to respond to an emergency situation that would not be possible in a smaller organization.

A centralized research and development organization will be more effective in generating and evaluating new technology. As noted in the discussion of technology inputs, new technology typically appears as an invader seeking to replace the conventional technology in use. A centralized R&D component is not intimately involved in the application of present technology; its people have little emotional and professional commitment to the achievement of their career aspirations through application or improvement of present state-of-the-art. They typically have broader contacts in the external scientific and technical community, and hence are in a better position to perceive new technical opportunities or threats arising from technical trends and achievements in the external world. Perhaps more important is that the centralized laboratory, with its broader scope and greater range of skills, is more likely to have the capability to create a truly different technology or to evaluate the applicability of a new technology developed elsewhere. The development of the vacuum interrupter —drawing on skills and techniques developed for semiconductors and electron tubes—as a potential replacement for circuit breakers on electric power lines is a classic example of the kind of contribution a centralized R&D organization can make.

The competition between the present and the new technology is another facet of the "creative tension" that this book advocates as an indispensable ingredient in innovation. The dedication of the practitioners of the conventional state-of-the-art *should* confront and compete with the advocacy of the developers of the new technology. The relative merits of the opposing approaches will be validated only in head-to-head struggle. One of the surest ways to abort an innovation is to assign responsibility for its pioneering application to the practitioners of the conventional art, with the announced purpose of insuring an "orderly" introduction of the new art. The cards are stacked against the newcomer. Under these circumstances it is likely that a competitor will soon demonstrate the virtues of the new technology to the reluctant practitioners of conventional art—and the transition will be anything but orderly!

The situation of the centralized lab with respect to extending the state-of-the-art is somewhat different. The extent to which such a group can contribute is heavily dependent on the degree of commonality found among the technologies required throughout the corporation. Frequently it will be found that quite different businesses have need for similar technologies in such fields as heat transfer, corrosion, mechanical behavior of materials, insulation, computation, and many others. Where this is true, a centralized organization permits a degree of specialization that facilitates the development of sophisticated expertise to serve as a backup for the engineers performing product development and design. This expertise flourishes where the situation permits long and continuous immersion in the field and exposure to a wide range of technical problems in the specified area.

Application of state-of-the-art is quite different. It is the heart of technical work in operations and can be centralized successfully only when there is a high degree of coherence in the basic technologies needed by the business, as is the case with AT&T. Even in this situation, where the business involves multisite operation, centralization imposes difficulties. This problem will be examined in more detail in Chapter 11. One may take as a general principle that the closer an innovation is to commercial realization, the more important it is for the work in *all* functions to be closely integrated. The birth of an innovation requires a continual tuning of the entire system, which can be accomplished only through intimate and virtually instant communication.

There are also some significant disadvantages associated with a centralized R&D organization. Probably the most important is that such a group finds it more difficult to couple with operations. Since the corporate laboratory is reporting at a higher level in the organization, it may be regarded as competing for funds and for status with technical components in operations. The central lab is not a part of the operating team as local management sees it; it isn't an integral part of the team, with a deep commitment to the objectives of the operating component. This insulation from operations is a particularly unfortunate deterrent in program planning, which hinders selection of projects that are consistent with business objectives and complicates assignment of priorities that match operating realities. Hostility and/or jealousy may lead to severe distortion and a censoring of information, but even with good intentions on both sides the cultural gap between them is exceedingly difficult to bridge. Communication of information in itself involves distortion and attenuation, which even great effort cannot eliminate.

The centralized organization also finds it more difficult to accomplish the transition of its outputs to operations. For one thing, a transition may involve a geographical separation, so that the output of the laboratory has to be transferred and applied at a remote location. Given the inherent communications difficulties in transferring technology from one group to another, a geographical separation imposes a severe and frequently a crippling, additional handicap. An even more serious impediment is the resistance of people. The saying "not invented here" (NIH) has been coined to popularize the reaction of people who have not been in on the work from the beginning and who frequently are somewhat less than enthusiastic about helping to develop it further. As a matter of fact, technical people in operations may feel affronted. They may regard a new development from a central R&D group as an insult to their own creative capabilities or they may have been pursuing an alternative approach.

Particularly in the early stages, the relative merits of alternative technical approaches are difficult to assess definitively. Consequently, claims by technical people in operations that their solution is simpler, or more certain, or more elegant are difficult to refute. In any event, attempts to overcome resistance by demolishing such arguments are essentially futile. In research and development there are a thousand ways to kill an idea, and people who are not enthusiastic about it can discover most of them. Consequently, progress depends on fostering support, not on destroying opposition.

On the other hand, the fact that an organization is divorced from the current pressures of operations tends to make its people overlook the time pressure required to achieve a solution to a problem. Consequently, the central laboratory may produce results that, while they are responsive to the problem at hand, are not timely with respect to the needs of the operation. In a similar fashion it may produce an answer more elegant than the situation permits. One of the hazards technical people must guard against is becoming so enamored of the elegance and sophistication of their own ideas that they advocate solutions that are more grandiose than the problems require and that would necessitate either more time or money to execute than the situation will permit.

Another disadvantage of a centralized lab is that an organization which is physically and organizationally separate from operations may not be sufficiently responsive to the problems that arise. The lab doesn't feel the same kinds of pressures, it isn't aware of all the constraints faced by people in operations, it may not be willing to stop what it is doing and respond to an emergency situation. The isolation recommended by some professionals as an ideal environment for long-range technical work is not necessarily appreciated by people in operations. The belief that the central lab cannot be depended on to respond to problems leads operations to establish the capability to solve its own problems, and thus the central lab is further decoupled from its most important outlet for its discoveries.

A final disadvantage is that, typically, the cost on a per-man basis —particularly visible cost, not cost per unit of output—is likely to be considerably higher in central organizations. These laboratories frequently become expensive showplaces for the company and are used for marketing and public relations purposes. Even more important is that they often contain expensive equipment and provide extensive technical support that is expensive, even though both are necessary for performing sophisticated, advanced technical work.

The merits and weaknesses of centralized R&D are not dissimilar in principle from any generalized discussion of centralized versus decentralized operation. The former permits greater specialization, is more amenable to control from the top (at least in principle), and is better coordinated, but it can also become resistant to change, detached from the reality of operations, and cumbersome to maneuver. R&D simply exhibits its own special forms of these attributes.

Decentralized Laboratories

The advantages and disadvantages of decentralization are almost the opposite of those mentioned for centralization. The most important advantage is that decentralized labs are organizationally and frequently physically a part of operating components and therefore they have the opportunity to become better integrated into the planning and into the operating team. Their physical availability permits frequent interaction and enables lab managers and technical staff to be better informed. They are regarded as sharing the same burdens, the same problems, the same vexations as people in operations, so that their communication can be more intimate than would be possible under more remote circumstances.

The objectives of a decentralized lab are more easily established, and this is a point that is frequently not sufficiently recognized. A central laboratory has a very difficult problem in trying to decide what contributions it should seek to make to the company and, particularly, how to distribute its resources over a variety of possibilities. In a smaller organization, with a more limited scope and serving more homogeneous clients, there is less uncertainty about what it ought to do and about the priorities associated with various programs. Finally, since it is organizationally a part of the local management team, inputs from the decentralized labs can be planned for as a part of larger programs that the entire organization is undertaking.

Since a decentralized lab will be organizationally and in many cases physically closer to an operating business, its programs are more likely to be subjected to a rigorous business review of objectives and costs. While its programs will tend to be more limited in scope and of a short-range nature, they will be integrated into the total business plan and provision for implementation of program results will be a part of the plan. Thus, transition of results to commercial application is made with less frustration and less lost motion than in centralized organizations. Largely as a result of this same careful review of costs, and also as a consequence of the less ambitious programs that a decentralized lab undertakes, the cost per technical man will typically be lower. The overhead associated with special equipment is less, salaries are typically lower, and controllable unapplied expense is more rigidly constrained. Some authorities will argue that this view of costs ignores quality of output, but even if it were possible to normalize these costs by some objective measure of technical output, there is still a considerable body of R&D work that can be performed at less cost in decentralized labs.

As noted earlier, a decentralized lab is particularly well suited to application of the state-of-the-art, to the application phase of extending the state-of-the-art, and to *applying* new technology. All technical work directly associated with application to specific products and manufacturing techniques is best carried out on the operating site under the direct control of the management team responsible for the success of a particular business.

On the other hand, there are some severe disadvantages to decentralization as well. The smaller size, as compared with that of a centralized structure, typically dictates reliance on less sophisticated and less complete resources, from the standpoint of both people and equipment. A more serious objection is that many such small organizations are not very flexible, partly because they do have limited resources. There are certain classes of problems they simply are unable to tackle because they don't have the requisite competence, and the need may be sufficiently infrequent to make it uneconomical to develop in-house competence. In some cases, decentralized labs don't have enough people to divert from scheduled work and assign to special projects. They are continually vulnerable to the threat of becoming too parochial in their outlook and missing the significance of external events.

Another disadvantage, particularly when viewed through the eyes of technical people, is that decentralized labs tend to be less stable. They are part of an operating organization with scope more limited than that of the total company, subject to vicissitudes, and buffeted by competitive pressures from which a central lab is insulated to some extent. Furthermore, work is more likely to be started and stopped in accordance with the short-run interests of operating management, making it more difficult to maintain consistent attention to long-range needs. Consequently, this environment is not attractive to many technical people who have devoted a substantial portion of their lives to acquiring highly specialized skills and who naturally want to capitalize on that investment. Decentralized laboratories are also less visible externally, and a decision to accept employment in one carries an implicit risk that the individual will become less marketable; therefore, the commitment appears to be less reversible.

The type of organization that seems appropriate for a particular company is undoubtedly a function of its history, of its geographical spread, of its technical diversity, of its general business strategy with respect to the emphasis placed on seeking competitive advantage through technology, and of its relative size and diversification.

Need for a Mixed Mode

Examination of the pros and cons of these various alternatives reveals an unpleasant dilemma. On the one hand, the kind of structure most attractive to highly competent people (the key ingredient in success) and which permits the most effective utilization of specialized equipment is some sort of corporate laboratory with a broad charter for technical work. Such a laboratory can be particularly valuable as a recruiting device for attracting highly competent technical people with advanced training. These people usually have had little practical experience and frequently are attracted to an environment that seems similar to the academic environment with which they are familiar. Thus, the corporate laboratory can provide opportunity for transition to industrial experience, and will attract many exceedingly able people who otherwise would go elsewhere. Needless to say, many of them remain in the corporate lab as scientists, while others move on to other positions in operations. On the other hand, corporate organizations of this type encounter problems in insuring the relevance of their programs to business needs, in producing results in a form and within a time scale that is suitable for operations, and in achieving satisfactory transitions of results to operations.

In a more decentralized approach to R&D, essentially the reverse is true. Coupling processes are generally improved, but resources are more limited, people are more focussed on application and extension of state-of-the-art, and are less specialized.

In choosing an alternative, the key questions should be: Which set of difficulties is more amenable to improvement and what kinds of technical inputs does the organization seek? The continuing severe competition for people of high competence, the trend for a high percentage of technical people to receive advanced degrees, and the growing sophistication and cost of R&D require that the availability of resources receive high priority in organization planning. Even the most diligent management efforts will have limited success in attracting competent people to a laboratory of restricted scope or in justifying the purchase of specialized equipment. If a company has assigned a key role to technology and expects to continue pioneering technical leadership as a significant element of its success, it has little choice except to separate at least part of its R&D operation from close association with operations. Otherwise, it is unlikely to be successful in generating and possibly even in recognizing new technology that can create a discontinuous advance. Conversely, if a company has chosen to emphasize factors other than technology and relies on its capability for rapid response to competitors' technical innovations, it will want to place R&D close to operations rather than centralize it.

If the company chooses centralization, it is important to recognize that improvement in the coupling processes *is* amenable to management attention. As we will see in later chapters, management *can* improve communications, it *can* improve the efficacy of transitions, and it *can* better integrate its planning with business objectives. Thus, emphasis in *organization planning* should be placed on providing adequate resources where individual preferences and outside forces are difficult to control, and *management effort* should be concentrated on improved coupling, both with respect to program formulation and to the transition of output to commercial exploitation.

Not surprisingly, perhaps the most common pattern for companies large enough to consider the alternatives of centralization versus decentralization is to choose a mixed mode in which the longer range and higher risk R&D work is reserved to a corporate lab while all other technical work is decentralized to operations. This arrangement naturally creates the necessity to establish the interface between the two. Organizational purists would argue that efficiency and effectiveness dictate that this interface be carefully defined with carefully delineated scopes for the respective organizations which clarify relationships, fix responsibility, and minimize the possibility of duplication.

Our thesis of the desirability of fostering creative tension as a necessary feature of the institutionalization of change suggests that efforts to achieve such clarity are misguided. Indeed, an organization structure that deliberately establishes overlapping, and to some extent competing, technical components is needed to facilitate the transition of R&D results to commercial application. This overlap is needed at every stage in the stream, from research to development to engineering to manufacturing, if effective coupling is to be achieved. The earlier discussion of the innovation process emphasized that each transition brings with it the risk of abortion, and a structure that provides for redundancy in technical capability at every interface facilitates the flow of the innovation through the system.

Thus, while the purists may shudder at poorly defined and even overlapping organizational charters, and those who see waste in duplicating or competing efforts will cringe, a truly effective organization from the standpoint of technological innovation will look mildly chaotic to all but the closest scrutiny. In particular, the general attitude with respect to organization structure and to funding must encourage the creation of ad hoc arrangements particularly suited to each transition. One may find the central R&D organization supporting application work in operations, to facilitate the transition of new technology. This demonstration of faith in the new technology on the part of corporate R&D management can help convince operating management of the validity of the opportunity and thus elicit its support. At the same time in another area one may find a competing team in operations trying to achieve the same objective by an extension of existing technology. One may also find a corporate laboratory engaged in quite prosaic design or product development work in order to remove an impediment to transition, such as the development of an electronic component with special price/performance characteristics needed for a circuit and which is not yet available on the market. Concurrently, a laboratory in operations may be engaged in some very sophisticated extensions of the state-of-the-art, such as the study of turbulence in the design of turbines or the analysis of electrical transients in electric power transmission.

Developmental Sequence in Organization Planning

It is interesting to note that there appears to be an almost inevitable sequence in organizational thinking with respect to R&D. When a research and development organization is first set up, its management feels a strong need to demonstrate its own autonomy. The lab tends to be rather apprehensive in feeling that it can be easily overwhelmed by the rest of the industrial structure; it is concerned with insuring that it gets good people and that it performs credible technical work. It tends to feel very strongly that only people who are in research and development will understand research and development and can suitably determine what should be done in the laboratory. Consequently, R&D management may be somewhat defensive and be a rather difficult partner to work with in its early days. A great deal of emphasis is placed on the need for isolation so that the work can proceed uninterruptedly and can be insulated from the pressures and problems of the larger organization. The R&D director tends to adopt the "advocate's role," described in Chapter 1. He defines his role as that of pushing as hard as he can for expenditures to be made on research and development, almost irrespective of other problems that the organization may face. The difficult task of comparing these proposals with competing needs is left to some higher authority.

With the passage of time this situation causes some severe problems. For one thing, the advocate's role is self-limiting; it means that one is not even regarding himself as being a member of the team. Furthermore, the businessman who has the severe problem of trying to allocate resources tends to become irritated with people who are always pushing for more and more without regard to other competing problems and other, perhaps more important, needs that have to be served. Unfortunately, the isolation in some cases leads R&D to advocate some programs that are indeed indefensible and thus serve to damage the credibility of the laboratory. Secondly, the isolation and the insulation R&D seeks does indeed provide continuity, but on the other hand it also makes the transition of results much more difficult. Consequently, R&D management may have little to point to in the way of commercial impact. The ability to obtain information about what the operating organizations need is also restricted by this same insulation.

As a consequence of the problems it accumulates, the R&D organization frequently begins to become defensive regarding the criticism it is receiving. Operating people become more and more aware of the funds that are being expended for R&D. They begin to question the adequacy of the outputs. They may even begin to say, "Should we have a laboratory at all?" At some point these circumstances create enough pressure to stimulate efforts to achieve more effective coupling. These changes may involve management, organizational, and even geographical changes to try to create a research and development organization that acts more like a member of the community. Sometimes the effort to establish a corporate R&D component is abandoned. Thus, paradoxically, an R&D organization may find that in order to survive and be effective, it must accept more constraints than it had been willing to accept at its inception, but in the process it may end up being more effective and having more influence than in the days when it functioned with great autonomy and jealously protected its role as an advocate of R&D.

Summary

We have been exploring the organization of R&D from an external vantage point, examining the factors that will affect the kinds of resources the laboratory will be able to acquire, the problems it will encounter in establishing coupling with the rest of the company, and the relationship between the mode of organization and the kind of work the laboratory is responsible for performing. The spectrum of decentralization versus centralization provides a convenient framework for such an analysis. Since the advantages and disadvantages of each are largely mirror images of the other, it is not surprising that, except in special situations of high technical coherence, most large companies end up with a mixture of the two. In designing this mixed structure, care must be exercised to provide redundancy in technical skills and point of view on both sides of each interface to facilitate transition. Moreover, the management attitude toward organization should be permissive with respect to the creation of ad hoc arrangements tailor-made to the needs of each innovation, if necessary.

11

Transition to
Commercial Use

As all inventors know, the path to commercialization is an arduous, rocky one. Most attempts fail to make it. Some of the principal differences between the small entrepreneur/inventor and technological innovation in a large company arise in this path to commercialization. In the small company, usually the same people carry out the entire process of innovation from creation of idea to commercial realization. Thus, the technical man who has invented something may find himself acting as a salesman, as a market researcher, or even as a financier in negotiating with bankers or with others for provision of funds. Naturally, he also has to be designer and production supervisor. Even if he is fortunate enough to team up with one or two other key people, between them they usually lack sufficient skills and background to be versed in all the aspects of business involved in bringing a product through to commercial reality. Thus, in comparison with a large organization these entrepreneurs may not perform some parts of the process very well, at least as viewed by a professional. In many cases they find themselves having to learn as they go, on a "do-it-yourself" basis. In contrast to the more knowledgeable and professional procedures in a large corporation, these efforts may look amateurish and inadequate in terms of the amount of data on which decisions are based and the skill with which tasks are pursued.

However, amateurish though it may be, this system has some very distinct advantages, principally arising out of the small coherent nature of the group involved in the task. First, there is no need to move the project from one group of people to another and attempt along the way to instill an understanding of its potential, a vision of where the project can go, and an enthusiasm for its probabilities of success. Thus, there is no lost momentum and risk of abortion is reduced. In that same sense, there is rarely a need for a physical transfer of the work and the equipment to a new location or for new equipment to have to be installed to take over the process at a new site. In many such cases the new equipment doesn't work well and considerable delay is encountered while the fledgling innovation is again put back on the track. This kind of move also nearly always involves a language barrier because the people who have been involved in the original creation and early development of the idea have developed a special shorthand and even a certain nonverbal understanding of the idiosyncrasies of the development that aids verbal communication immensely. Most important of all, there is a deep commitment to the success of the project on the part of the people who have been involved in it from the beginning. This kind of commitment provides the indispensable courage, faith, and persistence to drive a project through to success.

On the negative side, it goes without saying that of necessity such an effort by autonomous entrepreneurs must be small; if the project is successful, then a new crop of problems arises, principally those associated with handling very rapid growth. These autonomous entrepreneurial organizations are typically very resource-limited, both with respect to the financial resources available to finance growth into new markets and to enlarge productive capacity and with respect to the management talent to handle a much larger operation. The rock on which these organizations most frequently flounder is an inability to acquire at the appropriate time the new management skills to deal with the problems of very rapid growth and to manage a large organization rather than to cope with the problems of incubating an innovation.

Innovating within the Structure

The path of innovation in a large organization is essentially the opposite. The keynote to success in large organizations is specialization of people and talents. Thus, the path to commercialization typically involves a transfer from one group to another and a sequential involvement of people who are not initially involved in the process. The textbook sequence is to go from research to development to pilot plant to factory production and then to sales, along the way picking up talents in finance, production, and marketing, as the need arises, to keep the project moving. Thus, this path involves a whole series of selling efforts to bring new people into the activity, to instill in them the vision and enthusiasm of the original proponents, and to incorporate their work into the efforts of the team already involved in the project.

There are continuing problems of achieving commitment to insure that members of the groups have the same faith in the future of the project and a deeply personal involvement in its success. There are also continuing problems of language when new people must be made aware of the special terminology that has evolved and must establish the nonverbal intuition necessary for effective communication in a highly dynamic, relatively unstructured activity. And, of course, in many cases there is a physical move, with all the problems noted earlier.

One might very well ask why, in the face of all the difficulties and barrier problems created by this approach to innovation, specialization of talents is used, in contrast to the small coherent activity chosen in a small company. Why not copy the small company? In some cases, of course, large companies can do just that, and increasingly one finds "new business development operations" devoted exclusively to the creation of new businesses on a basis comparable with that employed by the autonomous entrepreneur. However, if a large company were to pursue this path exclusively, it would be giving up some of its very real strengths, one of the most important ones, of course, being the specialization that is so productive. Pilot-plant work, marketing research, financing, production planning, all can be carried on with a level of specialization and professionalism that is simply not possible in a small company. Probably a much more important consideration is the fact that most of the innovations must eventually be incorporated into the existing structure of the company. They typically represent extensions of, or natural adjuncts to, pieces of the corporation already in existence, or they simply modify an existing business in a significant way.

Establishing a series of isolated innovative efforts completely detached from the normal operation of the company leads to a kind of fragmentation that severely reduces the advantages of a large company. Furthermore, it entails walking away from one of the crucial problems all large organizations face—ossification. Technological innovation, with all its upset and controversy, is one of the self-renewing mechanisms that can help retain the viability of a large company in a dynamic world. This deliberate creation of mechanisms for change—the basic theme of this book—is analogous to staying in condition. The cardiovascular and pulmonary systems have to be made to work, to work hard in order to maintain tone in the human body. Similarly, organizations must be challenged; they must be forced to reexamine basic assumptions and priorities, to appraise strengths and weaknesses, to test their courage, and to feel the excitement of new horizons. Technological innovation is one way, perhaps the principal way, of providing such challenge. In my view, the large organization has no choice except to try to solve the problem of accomplishing the transition of innovative efforts within the framework of the existing structure despite the physical, organizational, and functional barriers that inevitably exist.

The Problem of Transition

There is no denying the seriousness of this problem of achieving the commercialization of R&D results. Almost any time R&D managers get together it becomes apparent that this transition is one of the most severe problems they face. When one listens to their conversations, one almost gets the impression that R&D people view the rest of the company as the enemy. They see themselves as on the attack in trying to force innovation onto the organization. It is also true that ineffective efforts in trying to introduce innovation can create strains and severely disrupt relationships in other aspects of operating the business. Other managers not involved in the innovation may feel they are being unduly pressured to generate cash to finance the new venture and are being denied attractive opportunities within their own purview. Furthermore, successful innovation involves a relatively high level of anxiety and a deep sense of commitment. Under these circumstances emotions are likely to run high, and feelings and opinions will be stated with considerable intensity. It is not surprising that controversy and severe strains in relationships often appear. When viewed through a microscope, even small revolutions (and innovation is a kind of revolution) appear to be scenes of great turbulence. The principal solace is recognition that it is better to do it to oneself than have it done by a competitor.

Recognizing the inevitable strains involved, management concerned with maintaining the long-term viability of the enterprise is vitally interested in attempting to make the total innovative effort more successful —to improve the batting average on successes, to reduce the time required, to minimize the resources consumed in the process, and to reduce the strain on people involved.

Aids to Transition

Jack A. Morton[29] of Bell Telephone Laboratories has provided a discerning discussion of the problem of accomplishing effective transition of R&D outputs into commercial application. Morton perceived the implications of the interaction between physical or spatial relationships on the one hand and organizational relationships on the other in influencing transition. His work, which has come to be known as the "barriers and bonds theory", recognizes the need in most large companies to have technological innovation involve both the geographic movement of the embryonic development from one location to another and its organizational movement from one component to another. The following discussion attempts to extend Morton's insight to make allowance for additional parameters that the manager can manipulate in his attempts to improve transition.

Both spatial relationships and organizational relationships can be either barriers that impede transition or bonds that facilitate transition. Close physical proximity can provide the easy interactions and contacts that maximize communication efficiency and help to spread the contagion of enthusiasm to all the people involved in the work. It also minimizes the delay resulting from misunderstanding or inability to acquire needed information possessed by others in the group. By the same token, physical separation produces deficiencies in these respects. Communication is inevitably less frequent and less efficient because the information needed frequently cannot be provided at the most opportune time. Enthusiasm is likely to wane because people are not close enough together to catch the spirit of progress, to revel in achievements of others, and to be spurred by competition so that they contribute their share to progress. Misunderstandings, confusions, or divergences in purpose can appear and persist for extended periods without people even becoming aware of their existence.

Being a part of a common organization also can provide a bond that provides a bridge for transition. The single organization is more likely to have the commonality of purpose that focuses effort. It provides easy mechanisms for discussion of objectives and agreement on common purposes, even mechanisms for resolving disagreement through formal channels if the necessity for doing so arises. Similar standards of measurement are more likely to be applied, and objectives and priorities of management are more likely to remain consistent and sustained. A single organization is less likely to stimulate the competition that almost inevitably occurs between groups, and it will typically provide opportunity for working with people who share common backgrounds, similar training, and points of view.

Again, for essentially inverse reasons, an organizational separation can be a severe barrier to effective transition of R&D developments. Reporting to a different boss inevitably creates, at least to some extent, the requirement to focus on different objectives. It will likely involve some competition between groups. It necessitates more cumbersome mechanisms for resolving disagreement and for getting decisions on courses of action. It frequently requires the participation of components whose fundamental purposes are not completely parallel or convergent and may even be competitive in some respects. At best, the area of commonality is only partial, and occasionally it is only a relatively unimportant portion of the combined scope of the two organizations.

Morton's key insight was in recognizing that, in seeking to accomplish transition, one can tolerate only one or the other of these two parameters as a barrier and still accomplish the transition of R&D results. In other words, one can tolerate physical separation of people involved in the accomplishment of the transition, provided they are parts of the same organization and report to the same manager; or one can tolerate organizational separation, provided the people are close together and have ready physical access to each other. Conversely, if the situation arises in which these barriers occur back to back, then the transition becomes virtually impossible. The barriers to effective communication are so great that it is virtually impossible for progress to be made.

The concept of physical or organizational barriers or bonds provides a very useful tool for the manager in seeking to plan a development project to commercialize a discovery by R&D. It provides guidance for him in choosing organizational relationships and it helps clarify the most appropriate course of action when physical separation is involved. The manager has a more rational basis for manipulating two of the key parameters at his disposal in seeking to improve the effectiveness of transitions.

What If Geography and Organization Can't Be Changed?

Unfortunately, the hard realities of actual situations are such that organizational lines cannot always be redrawn and groups that must be involved in the work may already exist in geographically separated locations. Despite the additional help that the "barriers and bonds" theory provides, it is still a limited arsenal for attacking all the barriers a manager has to overcome in accomplishing transition to commercial reality. Moreover, the manipulation of these two particular parameters is most useful in circumstances where transitions occur along fairly stable and repetitive channels. Where transitions are much more ad hoc in nature, with each being a special case, it might be inappropriate to set up a permanent new organizational relationship to attempt to deal with each situation. The management responsible for handling the innovation must be in a position to control geography and organization without undue upset to people involved and with some reasonable continuity for the arrangements established. Where managers have no such control or inadequate control over decisions regarding organization and location, they are not in a position to influence the transition process in an effective fashion.

Morton's analysis has emphasized what might be termed the "structural features" of the innovation process: Who are the participants and how should they be related? If, in addition, one examines the resource aspects of innovation, two additional tools that are amenable to manipulation by the manager become apparent. One of these tools is money; the other is commonality in level of training and point of view among the participants to the transition process. The use of these tools considerably extends the manager's arsenal for improving transition.

The potentialities of money as a tool of managerial action have by no means been fully exploited. For the most part, money is viewed in a simplistic fashion by people in R&D as a resource that permits technical work to be performed. If, instead, one views it in its traditional economic role, as a medium of exchange, a number of other interesting possibilities are opened up. When viewed as a medium of exchange, money can be seen as a way of negotiating common equities and mutual interests in a particular research and development project or innovation effort. Money becomes the common denominator by which various parties who are potential participants in a transition can indicate their true interest in it. Thus, negotiating for the support of a project is a way of identifying the extent of true interest on the part of the potential parties involved. Obviously this system cannot function unless the opportunities for providing support are relatively unfettered by company policy regarding the flow of funds. For example, a company rule that says the funds allotted to corporate research and development cannot be used for the purpose of demonstrating commercial viability severely restricts the ability of the R&D people to demonstrate their faith in the potential of an innovation by putting their funds into an internal joint-development project.

The negotiations that lead to an identification of mutual interests and then an exchange of resources for completing a transition are a way of forcing tangible commitment of resources to the success of the endeavor. This commitment can then become a very powerful integrating force for directing the energies and attention of the various parties to the transition toward its successful prosecution. The federal government has for years used money as a lever for attracting the attention and focusing the interest of people throughout the country on particular R&D projects. Money used in this fashion has overcome the barrier of both organizational and geographical separation and has provided the integrating force that unites otherwise fragmented organizations in pursuit of a particular goal. In an analogous way, a central R&D group can "buy" the interest of a development group in operations during the early stages of the transition when much faith is needed to invest in its potential.

Money has some unique advantages in being used as the medium for this particular kind of transaction. First of all, it is easy to initiate a flow of money from one group to another; it simply takes a decision and the stroke of a pen. In the same sense, it is easy to terminate a relationship. Thus, in comparison with the task involved in creating a new organization or in moving an organization from one place to another, money permits much more latitude in initiating and modifying transitions. Money is also an exceedingly flexible tool because it can be almost infinitely divided. There is no problem of the lumpiness of resources that one encounters when dealing with individual capabilities of people or organizational components. One has to hire or transfer whole people, but partial man-years of effort can be contracted for. Thus, participation can be divided up on a much finer scale than if one deals with human beings or organizational components. Furthermore, changes subsequent to the original decision are much less visible and frequently less painful to bring about than if one creates a special organization and then at some later date finds it necessary to disband the group.

Thus, in a situation where a manager finds that he does not have the opportunity for creating the organizational relationship that he regards as desirable and where there may be physical separation beyond his control, he may through financial control of the transition be able to provide a bond. Control of the purse strings can at least to some extent overcome the barriers created by physical and organizational separation.

I'm well aware of the fact that this situation can also deteriorate into a pathological situation where haggling over the actual division of funds in itself becomes a barrier to progress. The very flexibility and ease of subdivision of money can invite unconstructive bargaining beyond the point where any additional equity is being negotiated in the process. This is particularly true as the number of participants increases. However, the fact that a mechanism is subject to possible abuse should not prevent its use.

The Value of Commonality

The other mechanism that a manager has available to foster transition involves distributing technical work and technical people in such a way that there is commonality of knowledge and viewpoints among the people who have to participate in the transition process. This commonality is indispensable in establishing adequate communication. Any person who has struggled with the problem of attempting to provide adequate instructions for a neophyte in assembling, installing, or operating a new piece of equipment is aware of how limited is our capability for transferring information verbally from knowledgeable people to essentially unknowledgeable people. This problem is much more severe when one looks at the task of accomplishing innovation. Here, in many cases, the critical information required to transmit understanding and knowledge to new participants in the development may not even be recognized, much less conceptualized, made explicit, and codified in a fashion that makes it easily transferable. Under these circumstances any additional barrier, such as distance, to effective communication can prove to be disastrous. Conversely, people sharing a common technical heritage and holding a common commitment to the value of technological innovation can help surmount the barriers of distance and organization.

A manager can foster commonality along three different avenues. The first involves the creation of a common foundation in terminology, concepts, and methodology among the parties to the transition at every stage of movement, whether it be physical relocation or one involving a transfer to a new organizational component. In the transition from one group to another there must be people in both groups who have the same background, who are familiar with the same terms, who have used the same methodology, who recognize the limits and strengths of the particular techniques being used. These people can act as receptors and translators of information so that they can then pass it on to others in each group. Without this common foundation in terminology and methodology, the errors, misunderstandings, and inadvertent changes that creep in will be almost impossible to straighten out.

The second avenue to commonality is one in which the participants to the transition in the two organization components involved have equal status. If among the participants there is any sense of work moving from superior to inferior, this in itself will seriously impede effective communication. The people who are in a position of superior status will not receive sufficient feedback to know whether or not they are really communicating effectively. Conversely, the people who are regarded as lower status won't feel free to question intensively in order to insure that they really understand. Again, opportunities for error and misunderstanding will abound. The equality of status must be considered in two dimensions. First is the relative status of one party to the transition with respect to the other; as noted above, it is important for them to regard themselves as being approximately equal. The second dimension involves the status of each group in its local milieu. Almost certain to fail is an effort to transfer a project from a corporate laboratory to a laboratory in operations which is defensive about its local status in operations and which lacks self-confidence with respect to its ability to cope with the new development. Under these circumstances the local group is likely to feel threatened by the transition and will become a most difficult partner.

The third way to commonality must take into account the point of view in the two organizations with respect to the value of innovation itself. The task of transferring a project from highly enthusiastic, deeply committed people to a group of "doubting Thomases" over an organizational and geographical barrier is indeed a very difficult one. Unless some element of enthusiasm, faith, and persistence can be instilled, along with the confidence that the innovation is in fact worth investing the required time and effort, the innovation will be severely impeded. This point of view encompasses the entire management team in the operating component. It is commonplace in large multidivisional companies that some divisions are much more productive in technological innovation than others, even where there are no external differences to explain the variation. Part of the difference clearly lies in the differing managerial value attached to technological innovation. Where its value is depreciated, transition will be difficult.

The practical consequence of this need to provide commonality of language, of status, and of point of view is that the enterprise must provide for very substantial redundancy at every stage in the transition process if it is to succeed. One general rule of thumb is that if a geographical separation is involved, the transition must move at the same level in the technical spectrum. In other words, a research project transferred to another group must be transferred to a research group. After the transition over the geographical span has been made at the same level of technology, the transition from research to development can then be made in the new organization. If an attempt is made to transfer a *research* project from one group to the *development* phase in another physically separated group, the problems of language and viewpoint will almost certainly preclude successful transition.

The second practical consequence is that the transition is unlikely to succeed if it is undertaken as a part-time responsibility. It requires a level of commitment that is possible only if it is the full-time responsibility of an individual and if his very career rides or falls on the success of the undertaking. Thus, any movement of a project from one group to another must go from people who are deeply committed to the success of a project to another group of people whose entire careers are also bound up in the success of the undertaking. Perhaps the most useful steps that can be taken to facilitate the transfer of vision and commitment is to arrange for the movement of people. People who have been associated with the project in its earlier stages can move to the new group that is accepting the transition and thus help maintain the continuity of effort, or people can come from the receptor organization to work temporarily on the development in the originating organization. Not only can they acquire the terminology developed, but also they can absorb some of the momentum and enthusiasm, which can then be carried on to the new group. Increasingly one comes to recognize that effective transition of technical work is most likely to be achieved by movement of people along with the movement of the project itself.

Summary

As we have seen, the transition of a technological development to commercial exploitation in a large company almost inevitably involves movement along a human chain. People with the skills needed at succeeding stages of the process must be assimilated into the venture and somehow infected with the vision and dedication needed in order to achieve success. The managers responsible for this endeavor need all the techniques they can invent to make it work. This section has explored four specific forms of managerial action in trying to foster the bonds that support transition: arranging for physical contiguity, placing in a common organizational framework, extending financial support, and providing commonality of training, interest, and commitment along the transition path. Each form admits of a variety of modes of implementation, which can be used in various combinations depending on the circumstances. The key ingredient of all modes, however, is managerial commitment. Without an unswerving drive on the part of R&D management, laboratory achievements will never reach the stage of commercial application.

In an ongoing organization that has transitions and innovations under way in a number of different areas, one consequence of the effective manipulation of the four parameters defined above will be the creation of what will appear to be chaotic interface relationships. These relationships will appear exceedingly untidy to the management theorist who seeks clarity in definition of charter, regularity and systemization in assignment of responsibility, and order in the flow of funds. I would submit that the efficiency sought in eliminating all duplication and in seeking clear assignments of responsibility is actually counterproductive. The fact is that a laboratory which is physically isolated, which has a clear and unambiguous charter, which carefully delineates its scope from that of any other technical group in the company, and which has its funding very carefully supplied from a corporate source is liable to find that it has all the parameters mentioned—geography, organization, funding, and differences in point of view—acting as barriers to effective transition. Under these circumstances failure is practically assured.

What is needed is an arrangement that permits overlapping, and to some extent even competing, technical strengths at each stage in the stream from research to development to engineering to manufacturing, if effective coupling is to occur. In a situation being managed effectively from the viewpoint of achieving technological innovation, one is likely to find a variety of arrangements in existence. Some projects in the corporate laboratory may be supported by operating groups, some may be sponsored jointly by the corporate laboratory and operations, but also some projects may be supported in operations by the corporate laboratory and sometimes even by multiple funding from a variety of sources. One will find people with the same interests and background working on what looks like the same problem at two different physical locations. Examination will demonstrate valid reasons for the apparent duplication. In some cases one may even find pieces of projects split up among three or four different groups according to their capability, their interests, and their resources available at any point in time. In other words, it is well to adopt a flexible, adaptive point of view in manipulating the parameters that will influence innovation, rather than accept a preconceived notion of "sound" organization concepts imposed by higher level management. The key ingredient is a relentless commitment by R&D management to do whatever is necessary to see that its output passes the ultimate test—commercial application.

12 Technical Communication

Interest in technical communication arises from the need to insure that information flows to people who need it, that it is available when needed, and that it arrives in a form that is usable by the recipient. Many discussions of technical communications focus on communication among individuals or small groups in close proximity to each other and who share strong professional or organizational interests. At the other end of the spectrum is the attention being paid to technical communication on a global level, with efforts under way to improve the storage and retrieval of information so as to maximize the social utility of the enormous investment being made in research and development. The situation faced by large organizations is somewhere between these two objectives. Many of the precepts for improving small group communication simply are not applicable in a large organization. The storage and retrieval requirements being developed in national and international networks also do not adequately serve the needs of a large corporation.

More to the point, a large organization heavily engaged in technical work is not just interested in the goal of insuring that individual technical teams achieve effective communication among themselves and make effective use of external sources of information. A large company typically has activities across the entire spectrum, from people generating the most advanced and sophisticated new information to people who are simply applying the state-of-the-art. Its objectives in seeking effective technical communication

145

are multiple. It wants advanced technical specialists to be adequately coupled with their peers; it wants them to be in effective contact with those applying technology; and it also wants those applying technology throughout the company to be making effective use of the enormous reservoir of technical knowledge residing in the total company.

Problem of the Large Organization

If one is not careful, the large organization will have the worst of both worlds. If one views technical communication from the standpoint of transmission from source to locus of need, as though one were pushing a substance through a pipe, and asks how this process can be improved, the problem in a large geographically dispersed organization seems almost hopeless. People throughout the organization do not interact frequently; sources cannot easily identify needs, much less determine appropriate timing and manner of presenting information. That there is genuine cause for concern is reflected in the almost universal fear of management and technical people that they are "reinventing the wheel," the colloquial expression used to describe the duplication of effort that is inherent in a poor communication system. Wherever this occurs, the manager quite rightly feels that the large organization is failing to take advantage of the technical strength and coherence that should prevail in an integrated organization structure.

On the other hand, if one turns the problem around and asks how people who need information can be made more aware of their need, be motivated to seek information, and be aided in finding it, then technical communication becomes more amenable to efforts to improve it. Viewed from this perspective, formal and informal technical communication—the two classes of communication most frequently discussed—can be seen as complementary. If formal communication is defined not only as a means of transmitting information, but also as a means for creating a framework that can nurture informal communication, then the manager may have additional means available to improve the total communication process. In other words, if the manager cannot insure that people will talk to one another, he can increase the probability that they at least know each other, and he can make it easier for them to communicate if they wish to do so. In a large organization these steps can be crucial in improving communication.

One obvious approach to this subject is to list the various means of technical communication, classify them as "formal" or "informal," and then evaluate the potential contribution of each to the process. This task proves to be disturbingly difficult. Among the items on the list are technical reports, memoranda, letters, conferences, symposia, courses, seminars, visits, phone calls, temporary assignments, casual interactions, and the usual managerial chain of communication. If one attempts to classify these items, he is likely to end up saying, "It depends on what you mean by formal or informal." The terms "formal" and "informal" are seen to comprise a convenient dichotomy for what is really a spectrum in which the various means of communication are not easily delineated. Nevertheless, one recognizes that formal and informal technical communications are different in significant ways and that the distinguishing features should be clarified.

Formal Communication

The elements of more formal technical communication are distinguished by the following characteristics:

1. Explicit organizational responsibility to communicate to a specified audience on subject matter which is or can be categorized. The communication is more likely to be initiated by the person who has information to transmit.
2. Explicit provision for the channels of transmission. The transmission is more likely to be sequential through organizational channels so that the first act of communication starts a specified chain of action.
3. Explicit provision for recording either the content of communication or the act of communicating so that in principle the process can be monitored and the content retrieved.
4. The communication, whether written or oral, is more likely to be impersonal; i.e., it is usually aimed at classes of people, not individuals, and its usefulness to individuals varies widely.
5. Content is more likely to be cognitive than emotional. It is more likely to be factual than inspirational or interpretive.
6. Feedback on transmission, reception, and the effects achieved is cumbersome and tenuous. Consequently, assessment is difficult.
7. It is relatively low cost in terms of audience reached for effort

expended, but may be quite ineffective in terms of results achieved for effort expended.

Informal Communication

While the characteristics of less formal technical communications are largely the opposite, they are worth stating:

1. The initiation of communication is largely ad hoc; it is difficult to specify in advance who should communicate to whom, about what, and when. Furthermore, the initiator is likely to be randomly, rather than hierarchically, determined.
2. It is largely direct and personal among acquaintances. If it is segmented, the sequence is determined by substantive logic, not by organizational logic.
3. The content and level of activity are difficult to monitor and retrieval is difficult.
4. The content may be cognitive, but it is peculiarly useful for information that goes beyond factual content to provide evaluation or interpretation.
5. Feedback is rapid and extensive; consequently, assessment of effectiveness is simpler.
6. It is inherently more expensive in terms of audience reached for effort expended, but may be exceedingly effective in terms of results.

Differences in Use

Having characterized more formal and less formal communication, let us look at some of the differences in the ways in which they are used, including all the communication incident to the performance of technical work in support of a business. Even when a salesman sends in an order, he is generating a technical communication, as one will soon discover if the salesman has promised performance the product can't deliver.

First, formal communication is used to provide information regarding the organization itself: business plans, technical programs, schedules, progress reviews, etc. Second, it is used to inform regarding the process of communication itself: who is responsible for action or decision, who has information, what reports are required, etc. Third, formal communication is a means of mobilizing the organization's resources with respect to problems: what the problem is, what our response will be, how it will be implemented, etc. Fourth, but not least, formal communication is used to transmit technical information of a strictly scientific or engineering nature, largely in the form of reports.

It is this latter aspect of technical communication which most people have in mind when they refer to technical communication; for example, the diffusion throughout the technical community of the known facts (principles, findings, methodologies, etc.) that are being developed and practiced in the various fields of science and engineering. Within a large organization the principle objectives of this type of formal communication are: (1) to inform people throughout the enterprise of relevant R&D results that are being accomplished elsewhere within the organization so that the company will be able to take maximum advantage of its investment in research and development, (2) to call to the attention of people throughout the company the relevant results being accomplished elsewhere throughout the world of science and engineering, and (3) to provide a retrievable record of technical work.

By contrast, less formal technical communication serves principally to insure that people have, or can readily obtain, information directly pertinent to their particular needs. It is inherently ad hoc in nature. Thus, in many cases the recognition and definition of need will rest largely with the person facing the problem, and he is more likely to initiate the communication. In other cases it results essentially from a fortuitous contact between people. In the latter case a particular fact of importance is communicated without necessarily any intent on the part of either party for such an occurrence to transpire. In general, however, the factual content of informal communication is likely to be less significant than the evaluative or interpretive aspects. Typically, an individual is seeking help in making an interpretation of a finding, an evaluation of a conclusion or of information derived from some other source, or even in identifying an authoritative source of detailed information. Consequently, the source of information being solicited must be authoritative if it is to be effective.

Another function of informal communication is to influence behavior or action. This type of informal communication is more likely to be initiated hierarchically, where one seeks to deter, encourage or redirect the effort of other people. Perhaps the most important form of informal communication is the type that produces new ideas through the interaction of people who are considering a problem. Productive results are obtained from the interaction of people who have different backgrounds and different points of view and whose contributions culminate in the stimulation of new ideas that would not have been conceived by an individual working on the problem alone.

Improving Informal Communication

No attempt will be made to judge the relative importance of formal versus informal communication; both are indispensable if R&D is to be done in the most productive manner possible. Clearly, formal communication is more amenable to managerial efforts to improve it. However, the preceding discussion of the characteristics of more formal communication indicated that no formal system, no matter how elaborate, is likely to completely satisfy the technical information needs of an organization. The problem the manager confronts in trying to improve informal communication is indeed a challenging one because he is, in effect, attempting to influence a process that is inherently not susceptible to direct managerial control. In order for informal communication to occur, a person must recognize that potential sources of information exist, be willing to seek them, be able to identify them, and be able to gain access in a timely and convenient manner. Since it is largely a spontaneous act, a manager cannot induce it by fiat, and even suggestion will have only limited effect.

For the manager seeking to improve communication, perhaps the most important insight to acquire is the recognition that there is a strong interaction between informal and formal communication and that he must consider them together if he wishes to improve the total communication process. In considering possible avenues of action in trying to improve informal communication, a manager should consider both his own behavior as a manager and his opportunities for influencing communication through managerial action. His first opportunity to influence communication is in establishing the technical staff itself. A competent technical staff is the best possible instrument for achieving adequate communication. People who are incompetent are usually afraid to seek help for fear of exposing their inadequacy, nor are they sought out by others because they have little to offer; thus, they are relatively isolated. In contrast, highly competent technical people are strongly motivated to achieve personal eminence in their professional careers; they have no desire to waste time duplicating the work of other people, and they do not feel threatened by the work of others. Thus, unless unusual constraints are placed in their way, first-rate technical people will maintain a high level of communication with their peers in other places, on the basis of mutual interaction.

The second thing the manager can do is to avoid placing undue restrictions on the physical act of communicating. A manager, by his words and actions, quite obviously can place a high or low value on communication, and his behavior will be readily apparent to his people. Technical people who are geographically separated from their associates in many cases indicate that they do not actually feel isolated, largely because their manager is sympathetic to their problem and encourages them to maintain contact. On the other hand, if a manager demonstrates by his words and actions that he believes it is the individual's responsibility to stay home and tend store, he will create a barrier to communication which will indeed make people feel isolated. This area is a delicate one because a manager's words and actions will sometimes give contrary signals. At the overt level a manager may say he wants his people to maintain contact, but when asked to approve a trip he will frequently express doubt about its worth. His people soon get the message with respect to his true feelings.

Most managers want to do more than simply avoid inhibiting communication. The question is, what can they do specifically to encourage it? Two areas are susceptible to managerial action: (1) identifying and facilitating contact with sources of help, and (2) reducing the language barrier to communication. Because of the ad hoc nature of informal communication it is unlikely to occur unless contact can be established speedily and conveniently. As pointed out earlier, informal communication is not likely to transpire unless a person realizes that potential sources of help exist and that he can readily identify them and establish contact with them. His problem rapidly reduces itself to how many people he knows and how much information he is exposed to. Conversely, if the source of the information is aware of its potential value to a specific individual and can volunteer what is truly helpful in an acceptable manner, he can do much to stimulate communications and build effective relationships. Curiously, many of the things a manager can do to improve performance in this respect involve improvements in formal communication, an area more amenable to managerial action.

For example, the role of technical reports in aiding informal communication is all too frequently overlooked. Technical reports are, of course, a cornerstone of formal communication. On the other hand, the distribution of a technical report provides not only information on a specific technical subject, but also on people who are active in that field. Thus, it aids in identifying potential sources of additional help. If one queries whether these reports go to the people who need them, whether they are timely and are presented in a useful form, the answer is "sometimes," maybe even "frequently." However, such answers are clearly not an adequate response to the technical communication needs of an organization.

Technical reports serve two functions. First, they provide a written record on the state-of-the-art for people currently active in a given field. This information may be too sophisticated or specialized for people who are not deeply involved in the area. This leads to their second function which is to provide a ready source of reference for use by experts in talking with other people. Such references reduce the burden of supplying solicited information by enabling an individual to use them himself or to refer the interested party to them. One of the very important activities in informal communication is to call attention to, and provide interpretive background on, written sources of information. This task is made relatively easy for the expert if he can simply refer to a report. It frequently permits him to provide help where he would not be able to take the time to do a detailed personal study in the area to gather the necessary information. One of the busiest and most highly regarded technical consultants I have ever known provided most of his information by referring to a large private library of reports, papers, and books with which he was intimately familiar. Thus, in encouraging the creation of a formal reporting system and insisting on documentation, a manager is creating one of the major building blocks in an effective technical communication system.

Nevertheless, the juxtaposition of both formal and informal communication is necessary to achieve truly effective information transfer through documentation. People who are not experts are much less likely to be aware of the existence of a relevant report, and even if they are, they may feel inadequate to apply it without expert guidance, the sort of guidance that is normally provided informally. These additional sources of guidance are far more likely to be tapped if people are acquainted with one another. It is a fact of life that informal communication is unlikely to occur between people who are strangers. Since managers have great influence over the opportunities people are afforded to establish personal acquaintanceships with their technical associates elsewhere in the company, they have ample opportunity to strengthen this foundation for improved communication.

Sponsorship of, and attendance at, internal technical meetings are among the most useful devices available to managers for encouraging informal communication. The efficiency of these technical meetings in transmitting information to a large number of people in a short space of time is widely recognized. However, just as important is the opportunity such meetings provide for establishing personal contacts. In many cases these contacts may be even more important than the specific technical information obtained. These contacts are especially important to those outside a given field who need the information and its interpretation from those within the field to help them in their work. The problem is not to establish effective communication among the experts in a field, because they are likely to know each other anyway, but rather to insure the diffusion of the information they are generating to others who are not active participants. Meetings can provide an opportunity for people in a peripheral technical field, or even outside the field altogether, to attend and find out who is working in the field, to learn some of the important findings currently being made, and to establish personal acquaintances with the people working in the field. These acquaintanceships establish the basis for a follow-up on an individual basis.

There is considerable misunderstanding of the nature of the technical communications problem. The communication among technical specialists working in a common field is remarkably effective. Extensive probing among many technical fields indicates that, even in a large and geographically dispersed company, the people developing new technical information in specialized fields know who their technical associates are, what they are working on, and what sorts of exceedingly specialized assistance they can provide.

The chief problem is with those primarily involved in applying technology, particularly technology that is new to the business. These people do not know the field and the people in it, they feel inadequate in evaluating and making pioneering applications, and they need help in establishing liaison with the network of specialists from whom they can get the guidance they need. They need special attention in fostering informal communication.

Efforts have been made to encourage diffusion of technical information by creating formal directories of technical competence. It has become apparent that formal directories are unlikely to be used unless a prior contact has been established. One of the major hurdles to informal communication is the fear, real or imaginary, that the potential source of help will not understand one's problem in all its complexity, that he will propose a solution which is not feasible, or that he will use terminology and concepts that the searcher doesn't understand. Apparently this fear serves to prevent directories from becoming effective means of triggering informal communication. A person in need of help who turns to a directory is, first of all, not even certain he is selecting the right name in the book. The directory may be out of date, or he may have misinterpreted the specialty listed for the chosen individual. Assuming a correct choice, he still faces the hurdle of contacting a stranger and, in effect, exposing his own lack of knowledge in a given area by asking for help. Most people find it exceedingly difficult to place themselves in a psychologically inferior position to a stranger. Thus, the manager can nurture informal communication by encouraging attendance at meetings in order to build up a network of acquaintances through which informal communication will occur subsequently.

Technical Liaison

Professor Allen[81] at M.I.T. has called attention to the role of "gatekeepers," people who in an evolutionary fashion assume the function of accomplishing technical communication between groups. This activity is ordinarily undertaken out of the personal interest and competence of the people who develop the role. It is not a formal responsibility and may not even be visible to the management of the organization, but it is regarded as crucial to the effectiveness of the technical groups.

The particular role characterized by Allen is identified with the operation of relatively small, coherent groups. Where a significant physical distance exists, where many groups are involved, and where the technical interests are diffuse, such informal roles are unlikely to emerge. However, it is possible to establish more or less official technical gatekeepers who are charged, either on a full-time or a very substantial part-time basis, with formal responsibility for keeping aware of the course of technical activity in physically separated organizations and for insuring that adequate contact is maintained. Perhaps "switchboard operator" would be more descriptive of the function, since these people in many cases are incapable of carrying on the technical interchange themselves. Rather, they act as liaison people publicly identified as the ones to contact in order to initiate communication. They monitor the health of the communication between organizations and insure that people who ought to be in close contact are in fact made aware of each other and encouraged to establish the contact. The critical problem is to trigger the communication process, and designating these liaison people formally helps to make them visible to people who are physically separated. The person needing technical inputs can thus identify an easy first step toward establishing contact with a reliable resource.

Providing Redundancy in Scope

Still another step that is directly under the control of management is in the specification of organization boundaries, which was discussed in Chapter 11. Communication, both formal and informal, is seriously impaired when technical boundaries are established so neatly that no duplication of skills exists. People who have similar technical vocabularies and similar intellectual tools with which to attack problems are much more effective in their communication with each other. The organizational theorist's desire for orderliness can lead to the elimination of overlapping effort and thus frustrate the process of effective communication. There must be people at both ends of the communication chain who speak the same language if effective communication is to occur.

The matter of language must be considered along two dimensions. One involves the special terminology associated with each technical discipline. One needs physicists to talk to physicists or chemists to talk to chemists if effective transfer of specialized information is to occur. Where this relationship cannot be established, a serious impairment of communication is inevitable, and sustained managerial attention will be needed to foster any communication. An electronics business once tried to circumvent this problem by appointing one of its design engineers as a materials specialist, to couple with chemists in the corporate laboratory. The action was ineffective because the engineer, for all his competence in electronics, did not perceive the materials and processes problems of his business through the eyes of a chemist, nor could he translate the chemists' suggestions into effective action.

The second dimension involves moving through the spectrum of technical work from research to development to design to production, which was discussed earlier. If one is seeking to move a project in transition (particularly over physical distance) from one organization to another, the transition must first be made at the same level of the technical spectrum, i.e., from research component to research component and thence to development. If an attempt is made to move from research in one component to development in another component that is physically separated, the handicap of ineffective communication may well abort the venture. Sound organization structuring must recognize that building an overlapping technical effort is indispensable to effective communication and to effective progress in work. Recognition of this precept is exceedingly important because most line managers and financial people regard duplication as wasteful. In accomplishing technical innovation, exactly the opposite is true: Lack of duplication is wasteful and may be even fatal.

Summary

This chapter has examined the complexity of technical communication in large, physically extended organizations. The mutual reinforcement of formal and informal communication emerges as a key feature of an effective communication system. The differing needs of those who generate information as opposed to those who apply it suggest the importance of insuring that "appliers" are given extensive opportunities to establish personal contacts with "generators." Only by so doing will the user organization help insure that it is well coupled to advancing technology. Formal communications systems are necessary, but not sufficient for this function. One of their most important but latent contributions is to provide the basis for more effective informal communication. Since formal communication is more amenable to managerial action, a manager concerned about the quality of informal communication in his component would do well to examine formal communication, particularly those aspects that provide opportunity for broadened personal contacts.

13 Roadblocks to Communication

It is a truism that business success is heavily dependent on, and most management effort is devoted to, the delineation of objectives for the organization and the development of ways to implement these objectives. It is just as obvious that delineating objectives and formulating plans can occur only if there is truly effective communication among the diverse participants in the process throughout the organization. The people in production, engineering, finance, employee relations, marketing, etc., represent very diverse points of view and have quite different backgrounds. Yet they must learn to talk a sufficiently common language that they can identify their common purposes and develop means to integrate their effort toward achievement of these common purposes.

Incorporating a New Function in the Business Team

The need to incorporate a new element into this planning process poses a very interesting problem. This subject was introduced early in the book; let us now examine other facets. How does a new function join the business team? In order for it to do so, the members already playing on the team must learn something of a new language and learn how to interact effectively with a new group of people who have different backgrounds and different values. In turn, the new function aspiring to team status must learn the language(s) of the business team and must develop some means of converting its own traditional modes of communication to terminology and ways of classification and expression that will be meaningful to the present members of the business team. Much of the discussion in Chapters 6 through 8 was devoted to this problem.

It may seem a trifle ridiculous at this point to be talking about research and development as a new function. Corporate research laboratories have existed for at least 70 years. R&D nationally employs several hundred thousand people and involves an expenditure of about $32 billion every year. The fact is, however, that any new function finds that the mutual accommodation involved in truly joining the business team is a very slow, time-consuming process. The four classical functions of a business are still regarded as engineering, production, marketing, and finance. These subjects still receive the most attention in the curricula in schools of business administration. It is only in recent years that business schools have offered even a single course in the management of research and development or the management of engineering. The American Management Association established its Research Division only about 15 years ago. Professional technical and scientific societies have begun to establish occasional panel discussions or sessions on the subject of the management of research and development, but these sessions are regarded as peripheral efforts and are in fact undertaken with a bit of trepidation.

What is perhaps even more surprising is that it is possible for a function such as research and development to cease to be new, even to be used extensively by a corporation, and still fail to qualify as a member of the business team. With a bit of reflection, however, it becomes apparent that industrial organizations not infrequently make use of specialties that they don't truly incorporate into their business team and make an integral part of their internal structure. Perhaps one of the best-known examples is advertising, which typically is regarded as requiring specialized talents best purchased from external specialists. Two other professional groups that still fall largely into this category are medicine and law. The specialized skills of these professionals are used by the industrial organization, but their role is basically restricted to the exercise of their professional expertise.

In most industrial organizations, even those that have been involved in research and development for many years, all too frequently research and development is regarded as more or less of an appendage—albeit a highly valued one—of the organization. It represents a group to which specific problems are assigned for solution, from which specialized talents are sought as the occasion arises, and from which unexpected breakthroughs hopefully will come. However, R&D is not accepted as a participant in the deliberations that help to establish the objectives of the corporation and which formulate the plan for achieving these objectives. The reasons most frequently advanced for this state of affairs all have an element of validity to them. It is asserted that the people doing research and development wouldn't be interested in this kind of work, and in fact many of them are not. It is also believed that they wouldn't be good at it because it is not the kind of activity for which their specialized background has any particular pertinence, and many would not. It is also stated that it would not be a good use of their time, that they are too valuable and must be kept in the laboratory inventing instead of being wasted on work of this sort, and for some that is undoubtedly true.

By the same token, even though the subject isn't so frequently discussed, some would also assert that the language and the intellectual rigor that the R&D people would bring to business planning and operations would in many cases pose an intellectual burden on the other participants. Scientists and engineers have spent many years honing their critical faculties with respect to the validity and relevance of assumptions, data, and methodologies. They don't leave those skills at the door of the laboratory, and one must acknowledge that they sometimes insist on more rigor than the situation will admit. The thought of learning how to cope with the people in this demanding new function is in itself enough to discourage active efforts to incorporate it into the business team.

Furthermore, the requirements to make use of the R&D contribution and to try to include planning for the R&D function as a part of the overall business plan are intrinsically very difficult tasks. It involves thinking on a time scale that may exceed the time span of much normal business planning activity. It involves consideration of risks, which people can't contemplate with unalloyed pleasure. It requires a fundamental examination of the purposes of the business, which is not easy to wrestle with. Since R&D frequently creates change, its pursuit requires candid evaluation of the capability of present management to accommodate to, much less to manage, the introduction of the change generated by R&D—a sometimes painful process.

Nevertheless, an indispensable part of the maturation of a function, and an absolute prerequisite for its becoming truly effective, is that it must become an activity that is understood and whose role and contribution to the organization are accepted by other participants in the ongoing life of the corporation. Where one finds that a major personal function of the R&D manager is to act as a mediary between the work of his group and the rest of the enterprise, and where he devotes large amounts of effort to translating the needs and contributions of R&D to the rest of the firm and also to reflecting to the R&D people the objectives and needs of the parent body, I think it is fair to say that R&D is not yet truly a member of the business team. Effective team participation demands a rich and extensive network of interaction, with many participants operating in a variety of modes.

Barriers to Communication

The persistence of ineffective communication over a long period of time is a clear symptom of the existence of major barriers or roadblocks. In R&D these barriers exist at three different levels, which we might term technical barriers, perceptual barriers, and value barriers.

Technical Barriers

The technical barrier arises when the terminology and the techniques of research and development are highly specialized. Many of the terms and concepts are regarded as esoteric by ordinary citizens, and they have indeed acquired highly precise meanings to the professionals involved. Thus, there is a genuine problem in finding some way to communicate the significance and meaning of the language of science and engineering to businessmen who do not necessarily have technical backgrounds.

While this problem is complex, it is generally quite obvious but solvable. If a physicist is talking to a public relations man or an accountant, it is apparent that he will have to use some care in choosing his words if he is to convey meaningful information about his specialty. Many first-rate technical people are also remarkably skilled expositors of science. Moreover, efforts to solve this problem have generated a field of specialists in technical communication, and considerable resources are now available for translating the terminology of research and development into language that will be understandable to the layman. Thus, while this barrier is most frequently mentioned, it is actually the least significant.

Perceptual Barriers

The second category of roadblock to communication, perceptual barriers, is not so tractable because these barriers are not easily recognized and their effects are insidious. For example, every profession tends to develop its own particular mode of discourse. By this I mean that some internal structure guides the use of the technical terminology. It involves such simple things as the accepted way to present information. The accountant typically says, "Let me see the numbers." He presents information in tabular form rather than graphically. The engineer is more likely to say, "Let me see the graph or curve." Evidence presented in an unfamiliar manner makes people uncomfortable. It takes more effort to understand and the risk of misinterpretation is greater.

There are also differences over accepting the relevance or usefulness of evidence, even the validity of evidence. The scientist or engineer is deeply suspicious of nonquantitative evidence. He tends to regard it as subjective and unreliable. He attempts to present evidence in terms of physical processes or as analogues to physical processes. The lawyer is very much concerned with precedent and tradition and with precision in the choice of words. Marketing and advertising people emphasize ideas, concepts, and dramatic appeal. All differences of these types tend to create barriers and impediments to achieving effective understanding. Furthermore, they tend to generate emotion and suspicion, which on occasion provides an additional barrier worse than the root problem.

The second principal source of perceptual barriers arises from the tendency of people to adopt a grossly oversimplified view of the complexities involved in the work of another. One unfortunate consequence of this simplistic view is that one is inclined to underestimate the constraints under which another person is laboring and thus regard him as either inept, uninterested, or too timid, when in fact the problem may be that one simply doesn't appreciate his difficulties.

This oversimplification is particularly unfortunate when one is attempting to introduce technological innovations. All too frequently the inventor or innovator, who is pushing a particular idea, fails to appreciate the difficulties that the marketing and manufacturing or even the engineering people may see in trying to reduce the idea to practical application and make a commercial success of it. People from research and development activities who have had direct exposure to business operations, who see the effect of market and economic forces, of labor relations problems, and who see the impact of competitive pressure often discover that life in the business world is far more complicated than they had appreciated. They come to realize that people in operations who don't move as rapidly as they had previously wished aren't necessarily the dumb dodos they had accused them of being. In fact, operating people are exceedingly capable, highly motivated individuals who have their own specialties to pursue and who are operating under constraints and limitations to which the people in R&D frequently have been totally blind.

This awareness of life in operations is especially pertinent in connection with the pressure in business to create and achieve the certainty that was described earlier. People who have transferred from research and development to operating activities discover that one of the real shocks to which they must adjust is the extent to which the plans in operations are intended to be achieved as stated. A good friend who transferred to operations told me that recognition of the fact that operating plans "had teeth in them" was the biggest adjustment he had to make. Transferees discover that there is great pressure to meet the objectives established because the work of other people is geared to this same set of objectives, and failure in any part of the system can make the entire exercise fruitless. One isn't permitted the excuse that "nature didn't cooperate—therefore, the work can't be done as planned." This kind of constraint tends to introduce a conservatism in planning and a depth of detail which is new to R&D people.

What Is Practical?

Although perceptual barriers to communication apply to a large variety of terms and subjects, let us concentrate on three areas that are of particular significance in research and development. The first is, "What does practical mean?" When a scientist or technologist says something "works," his meaning is quite different from that of a manager of production or even an engineer engaged in design. When he says that something is practical, or that it works, the scientist usually means that in his laboratory, with him and his technician hovering over it, the thing can be kept functioning—and when it doesn't function they are able to figure out why it has broken down and what sort of adjustment is needed to get the device functioning again or to bring the process back under control.

The scientist doesn't ask himself whether the device or process or machinery would last for ten years. He doesn't ask himself how much abuse it would withstand and still function. He doesn't ask himself whether one could make 100,000 of these devices and all would operate with acceptable similarity. At his stage of activity there is a whole range of phenomena and occurrences that are essentially extraneous to his objective, but which must be dealt with later. His concern is in demonstrating that a particular principle is in fact exhibited by a piece of machinery or device, or that a certain predicted end result can in fact be achieved. I well recall the sense of wonder with which one man described a general manager's instructions to have something "working." He said, "You know when he says 'something that works' he means he wants it to work 24 hours a day, 7 days a week, 365 days a year!" And that is exactly the kind of precision and certainty that the normal manager of manufacturing does indeed seek.

The work involved in reducing an invention to practice and even in demonstrating feasibility is only the tip of the iceberg in the effort required to perfect the combination of design, specification, and manufacturing process that permits consistently repetitive manufacture of a product, which is the goal of the production man. Progress toward this goal requires an excruciatingly painstaking and arduous evolution of detailed knowledge to which both the technical pioneer and the eventual user are largely blind. The level of perfection required and attained routinely in manufacturing constitutes both a remarkable achievement and a barrier to displacement by an upstart technology.

What Is Economic Feasibility?

The second term or concept that is a frequent source of confusion is the meaning of the term "economic feasibility." The scientist and advanced technologist is, at least generally, aware of the problem of scale and of the fact that something produced in very small quantities on a laboratory bench, or even in a small assembly unit, isn't necessarily ready for full-scale production. While the man in advanced technical work is not necessarily equipped to solve these problems, he is at least aware that they exist and that a special kind of skill and know-how are required in order to solve them. On the other hand, a true appreciation of the inexorable pressure that exists in any production organization to keep the plant running, to get material off the shipping dock, and to meet schedules at acceptable quality and cost is difficult to obtain vicariously. It necessitates a way of life totally foreign to the existence of the man in R&D. He has rarely faced the problem of having to go to a customer and explain that the delivery date isn't going to be met, or that promised level of performance will not be achieved; nor has he had to explain to a general manager that a projected cost cannot be kept within promised limits.

Advanced technical people are typically uninterested in and poorly informed about the entire subject of investment, of the amount of money that will be required to bring a process on-stream or to bring out a new product, of the availability of money for that activity in competition with other activities in which the business must engage, and of the potential payoff in relation to the costs that will be incurred. The fledgling innovation must compete for resources in a "no holds barred" struggle for the favorable attention of people whose commitment is to obtain maximum return on investment. They have no particular emotional attachment to the innovation or even to achieving competitive success through technology, for that matter. These people are beset by special pleaders for a host of investment opportunities, and quite understandably they must develop a considerable skepticism if they are to survive.

Managers of engineering complain that the biggest single barrier to innovation is the time required for and the cost of tooling. Timing introduction to market is crucial to success in innovation and the time delays required to acquire the tooling necessary for the high-volume production of large companies greatly increase the risk and complicate the problem of managing technological innovation. Yet the full complexity of manufacturing technology is a subject that receives scant attention in most R&D organizations.

Technical people also have little or no experience with, and therefore have little or no awareness of, the difference between having a process run with laboratory technicians and having it run with the kinds of people who are on the shop floor, where turnover may be high, training inadequate, maintenance standards minimal, and standards of acceptable performance may be quite different from that attained routinely by technicians.

Another area of misunderstanding related to economic feasibility involves the availability of raw materials. The mere fact that something can be made in small quantities doesn't mean that adequate materials or adequate parts are available at an acceptable price, acceptable performance, and with adequate assurance of continuity of supply. Particularly for new inventions, the supporting industrial infrastructure that feeds the production system may be nonexistent or maladapted to the newcomer.

What Is Marketable?

Perhaps the touchiest perceptual barrier of all is what is marketable. One of the most frequent complaints of scientists is that they invent something new, they propose a new product or new process, and then they are told it has no market. They are inclined to say: "People in marketing never want anything new. All they see are the problems associated with what you're doing. They aren't willing to get out and work to develop the market for a new product, or they lack the vision to see its potential." In many of these cases the scientist has acted as his own expert in assessing the marketability of a product. He makes his own assessment of the attractiveness or utility of a product or service by saying, "If I were a potential customer I would want this—therefore, there is a market for it." The man in advanced technical work has little background to prepare him to appreciate the painful problem of relating costs to value as perceived in the eyes of the potential user. He very rarely has to face the problem of having a potential customer say, "Yes, that's a fine product and I want it if I can buy it for less than $100"—and then having to go back and look at costs to find that it can't possibly be produced and sold at profit for less than $150.

Interestingly enough, one of the key steps in converting an invention into an innovation is the identification of just what features are regarded as valuable by the customer. One discovers with astonishing frequency that the properties which caught the eye of the inventor are not the ones that sell the product.

Technical people working in R&D typically do not worry about the application barrier involved in the introduction of a new product. It may have many valuable attributes, and in fact it may provide services the customers want, but these customers have to be educated in its use; they even have to be motivated to undertake the education that is necessary for them to use the product successfully. Thus, the process of creating a demand can be slow and costly.

Perhaps most important of all, because it seems nonsensical to the technical man, is the barrier imposed by distribution systems. For example, R&D may discover a fine product which appears to be attractive in the construction industry. However, if the enterprise has never called on a

contractor, its salesmen have no idea what contractors are like. Furthermore, the organization may have no credibility with contractors. Neither
does it have a full enough line of products to warrant contractors taking time
out of their busy lives to talk about special items. Because of these hurdles,
the product may appear exceedingly unattractive to the marketing people.
The barriers imposed by distribution and the concern over how to get a
product to market may seem almost irrational to the technical man, but they
are absolutely crucial to the businessman who has a product to move.
Knowing where your customers are, who they are, what their characteristics are, and how to contact them at a cost that one can tolerate, all comprise
crucial information if one is to get a new product into the market successfully. If this information is lacking, as it frequently is with supply-pushed
innovations, it increases the risk enormously and it also enlarges the investment and effort required to nurture the innovation.

Living with Uncertainty—The Technologist's Burden

The remarks made thus far suggest that most of the difficulties in
communication involve misunderstandings in or limitations of the perception of technical people. Not all the roadblocks to communication exist on
the side of the R&D people; just as many are problems in perception on the
part of the people in the rest of the enterprise when they view advanced
technical work. One of the most important is a misunderstanding of the
psychological burden imposed by the necessity of living with uncertainty.
In many cases the reaction of people in manufacturing and marketing, who
have to live with what they regard as the hard facts of life in attempting to
create and achieve certainty in business operations, is that life in research
and development is so easy! Deadlines don't have to be met; the constraints
under which people work are fuzzier; objectives are much more difficult to
measure; there is more room for error and sloppiness in planning and
operation, which is hard to detect; and one always has the excuse that
nature simply didn't make it possible. Thus, they insist life in this more
forgiving environment just has to be more pleasant. Jocular references to
the ivory tower or the country club are a part of life for R&D people.

In truth, living with uncertainty generates its own particular set of
problems. One of the most severe is the problem of working day by day
without knowing whether or not the work that one is pursuing will have any
productive result. One can even work in a field for a number of years

without knowing whether it is the right field to work in, whether one will achieve measurable results, or whether the effort will in any sense be commensurate with the final reward for achievement. Thus, one continually risks the possible loss of personal satisfaction that is associated with making a contribution, with feeling that one has achieved a desired goal and has found it worthwhile. This uncertainty creates a kind of anxiety that many people find intolerable. I once interviewed a man who was leaving a laboratory. He explained that for years he had sought to be transferred to R&D, but that once there he couldn't stand the uncertainty. He just wasn't cut out to wait five years before knowing that his work was successful or even relevant. The important point is that the R&D system can be "unfair" in that even great skill and intense effort will not necessarily lead to commensurate results and rewards.

Furthermore, and perhaps more important, one loses time out of one's life for which there is no way to compensate. One perceptive manager pointed out to me that he could protect people against the risk of failure in the sense of insuring that they weren't hurt financially, and in the sense of insuring that the uncertainty inherent in their problem was recognized and that the caliber of the professional effort they had put into it would be kept in perspective. But he said there is no possible way that he could make up the time, could give back the number of months or years that had been put into a fruitless project when something more worthwhile might have been done instead. We all recognize the pleasures of success in innovation and we know that, statistically, these successes are balanced by many more failures. But we rarely translate those abstract failures into human cost—good people who strove mightily to succeed and failed through no fault of theirs. Many people find it impossible to live under conditions that impose this kind of uncertainty. They need not only the pressure generated by the certainty sought in operations, but also the sense of security obtained through measurable progress toward goals in a relatively short time frame. This feature of R & D is rarely perceived by those not a party to the process.

Another perceptual barrier to communication arises from the failure of the layman to appreciate the almost mystical manner in which a technologist equates knowledge with the ability to make reliable quantitative measurements, measurements that necessitate exceedingly precise definition of terms and specification of the conditions under which the measurements were made. The technologist's barely concealed scorn for "subjective" knowledge not only places the nontechnical man on the defensive, but also can lead technical people to obstructive behavior in situations where time or the state-of-the-art do not permit generating the "reliable" data they demand.

In their own way, scientists are also seeking certainty—the certainty that their techniques and methodologies can be used productively. Whereas the business manager seeks to achieve certainty by scaling down objectives until they are likely of attainment, the scientist simplifies and restricts questions until they appear answerable, makes simplifying assumptions, or substitutes analogous systems that appear more tractable to investigate. Each of these actions tends to abstract the problem from the real world and to create the problem of translating results into steps applicable to the real world. People in other functions—marketing and manufacturing particularly—must accept problems in all their complexity because their goal is effective action, not rigorous understanding. These differences are not always recognized, and parochial pride leads to mutual denigration, which can generate hostility, lead the respective parties to doubt each other's competence, and effectively prevent convergence toward a consensus.

Value Barriers

The third class of communication barriers, "value barriers," comprises fundamental problems in interactions between people, which are perhaps the most intractable of all. They involve differences in life style, differences in priorities over what is important and unimportant, and differing interpretations of what constitutes progress. These same kinds of differences are very pronounced at the cultural level, where one observes the problems that arise in attempts to communicate with people in foreign cultures and how easily one can inadvertently create misunderstanding through both words and behavior.

People acquire different value systems as a consequence of a complex combination of the family heritage in which they have grown up, the particular community or communities in which they have lived, the schools they have attended, the individuals they've known, the experiences they've had. This complex of circumstances gives each individual a unique way of looking at the world. Nevertheless, some constellations of values tend to be associated with particular professional careers and particular styles of life. I should like to discuss three of these differences in values as they affect communication between technical people on the one hand and businessmen on the other.

The first has to do with the significance attributed to time. Businessmen regard time as the independent variable and the event or process as the dependent variable. They choose a unit of time and then, on the basis of this interval, identify or select events that will transpire or processes that will be carried to completion. In a crucial kind of way, as the businessman orders his universe, time becomes the dictator of events. Consequently, one of the important ways in which businessmen judge the behavior and competence of another person is the extent to which he can respond with what they regard as the right sense of urgency to any given situation. The ability to keep one's priorities with respect to time in proper perspective, despite personal predilections and changing circumstances, is one of the most prized traits. Based on this scale, scientists are frequently regarded as pretty poor performers in that they are inclined (in the eyes of the businessman) to get more interested in the process at work than in accepting the need to "cut the suit of action to fit the cloth of time," irrespective of the intellectual caliber of the result produced.

A related facet of the problem is the tendency of businessmen to digitalize time. Perhaps because of the convention of annual reporting of results, time is divided into equal packets that may have little relevance to the time constraints of the business. Scientists, on the other hand, tend to regard time very much as a continuum. Events or processes dominate. This originates partly from their strongly felt belief that one can't schedule discovery or invention; therefore, it is irrelevant to introduce time as a measure of progress toward discovery in this sense. A scientist can tell you how much work he expects to accomplish or to perform in some given unit of time, but he can't tell you how much progress toward any given objective he will have made by doing so.

Viewed in this fashion the tendency to talk about long term versus short term can be seen as an ineffective way of describing differences in time perspective. It is better to talk about time-dependent and time-independent processes. Time-dependent processes can in fact be scheduled and progress can be measured along specified intervals. Time-independent processes may in fact be either short term or long term in their completion. The important thing is that time is not an effective way of describing progress toward a given goal. When a researcher is seeking a cure for cancer, he cannot say, "I will be 50% completed in six months." This distinction may be a useful way to distinguish between research and development, a distinction that has meaning only within the R&D community. A manager once commented, "When work reaches the stage that I can schedule its completion, I regard it as having moved from research to development." This is not to say that one cannot plan and schedule what will be done in research; first-rate research people know in remarkable detail the sequence of their research for months or maybe even years ahead. The point is that they can schedule activity or process, but they cannot schedule progress—and the executive is interested in the latter.

The significance of this difference can be observed in looking in detail at much technical work. There is a tendency to believe that long-term projects are by definition "high risk," uncertain of completion, and typically are more associated with research than with development. In fact, one can observe many technical programs that are exceedingly long run in nature and where the risks are high, yet which can also be precisely programmed and scheduled, and have little research content—for example, the Apollo project. It is important to understand this distinction because it is the cause of much confusion. The risk with Apollo was principally with the time and cost required. Among scientists there was virtually no question of whether the goal could be achieved, with the possible reservations of unknown hostile factors in the space environment and man's response to prolonged weightlessness. Van Allen's research early in the space effort helped to reassure on the first point and precursor orbital flights helped reassure on the second. The challenge of Apollo was to organize and apply man's vast reservoir of knowledge to the solution of one particular problem—putting a man on the moon. The Apollo program stimulated much valuable research in plasma physics, celestial navigation, electronics, etc., but this research was not central to the completion of the mission. Similarly, Apollo made possible exciting discoveries in astronomy, earth science, and lunar science, but again they were not central to the mission. None of these qualifications on the nature of the work should deprecate the significance of the accomplishment; it was truly memorable. They merely point out that long range versus short range is not a useful way to distinguish between research and development.

In contrast, in the case of time-independent activities, progress may never come or may come in short order. There is no way of knowing in advance. These differences in attitude toward time as an arbiter of progress can create frustrations and animosities when people seek to work together cooperatively, and can lead to accusations of impracticality on the one hand or of being unreasonable on the other. Businessmen accuse scientists of being unrealistic with respect to business pressures and of being unwilling to make firm commitments for attaining goals; and scientists accuse businessmen of being unreasonable with respect to understanding the nature of technical work. There is a measure of truth on both sides.

The second major value barrier to effective communication arises from a difference in orientation toward action versus knowledge. The training that technical people get in school, and the entire tradition of progress in science and technology, emphasize the intrinsic economy of the general solution to a problem. People in R&D take as an article of faith a more precise view—that until one *understands* what is going on, until one can make a general statement explaining the mechanisms at work and can predict the results of a given sequence of events, one cannot deal in a truly efficient fashion with the phenomena involved. They believe that the creation of a general level of understanding or of a reasonable working hypothesis reduces the effort required to find solutions to particular problems. It minimizes the number of false starts that have to be made and the likelihood of subsequent unpleasant surprises; it increases the certainty that in fact a process or a product will work as specified. While they accept the inevitability of empirically based action, their entire thrust is to replace empiricism with theoretical understanding.

The businessman, on the other hand, is clearly action-oriented. His point of view is: I've got to decide. I must choose a course of action. If I have understanding, fine; if not, I still have to decide, and the understanding can come along later. He is also aware of the fact that much of the world's progress has resulted from brute-force solutions with understanding coming, if at all, at a later date. This circumstance applies to much of innovative work in which progress comes from what is sometimes termed "turning over stones." This approach may not be economical of effort, but it produces results, which in many cases exceed the progress that would derive from seeking to achieve understanding before initiating action.

These differences in viewpoints frequently cause conflict over the course of action to follow. The scientist feels exceedingly uncomfortable in taking action with respect to a process or phenomenon that he doesn't understand. He distrusts ad hoc solutions. He tends to emphasize the risk associated with pursuing a course of action which is not guided by understanding. The businessman, on the other hand, is aware of the fact that in many cases the alarms raised by scientists have proved unwarranted. He believes that even if trouble is encountered later, it is better to initiate action and take the risk of further trouble than to lose the time required to seek a general solution.

The paradox is that at one time or another each protagonist will prove to be right, and it is exceedingly difficult to determine in advance in any given situation which approach will prove more sound. I believe that this difference in point of view creates a permanent state of tension which should be accepted as a needed adversary process. In effect the scientist is being asked to be a devil's advocate, and while such a role is sometimes frustrating, it is a perfectly legitimate one.

The third value barrier to communication is perhaps a good deal more likely to arouse emotions because it involves differences in viewpoint over the role of profits as a measure of success in our society. A businessman accepts as an act of intrinsic faith that profitability is the most appropriate *single* criterion for measuring achievement and for guiding decisions on priorities and on resource allocation. It is the fundamental unit by which all business actions eventually are judged, and it has the great advantage of being operational. It is important to understand the impact that this basic belief has on the work of marshaling resources and on motivating businessmen. For the businessman this fundamental belief in the use of profits as a measure of progress, both personal and organizational, is a tremendous simplifier. It reduces to a common denominator a spectrum of alternatives and thus contributes to and even largely creates the decisiveness and efficiency that are generally attributed to business in contrast to other social institutions. When one is not quite sure what he is trying to accomplish, it is much harder to decide whether one is doing it effectively, and it is difficult to mobilize human resources for effective pursuit of diffuse uncertain goals.

This strong belief in the social value of profits and in the validity of profitability as a criterion of success makes it possible to organize the huge resources committed in the major industrial organizations in the United States, to integrate their work, and to measure the relative efficiency with which various parts function. Therefore, while the technical innovator might wish for a set of criteria that gives better recognition to the noneconomic values of his innovation, he might find that the existence of such a set could simply overload the managerial decision-making capability and thus create delay and fuzziness in decision making. Other social institutions such as education, government, and health care, which operate with less clear-cut criteria of success, have not been notably fertile ground for innovation.

Technical people, particularly those involved in research and development, believe as a fundamental tenet of their philosophy that in the long run their contribution to human knowledge has a beneficial effect on society and is a measure of personal success and of progress. This is not to imply that all scientists are strongly motivated to contribute to human betterment; some are simply doing what they enjoy, with little regard to its social utility. While in many cases scientists recognize the value of profits as a measure of some aspects of human affairs, they are more likely to include it in a long list of criteria used to judge both personal and organizational success. Thus, their measurement of progress and of contribution consists of more diffuse criteria than those applied by the businessman, and they see progress resulting from accomplishment in areas where the businessman is skeptical of the value produced.

The counterpart of the businessman's commitment to profits as a measure of social utility lies in the scientist's commitment to a belief that the physical world can be explained by rational processes and that the methodologies of science are the key to such understanding. To him, every advance in science is not only a step toward a fuller understanding of nature, but also an affirmation of the validity of scientific methodologies. Not surprisingly, he places a premium on the value of such advances because it reaffirms the worthwhileness of his commitment to science. Thus, the bedrock belief of all scientists and businessmen is founded on differing bases. They do not necessarily deny the validity of each other's position; they just start from a different point, and this difference is the basis for fundamental interpretations of value in their respective fields.

These fundamental differences in value associated with time, with the appropriateness of knowledge versus decision and action, and with the appropriateness of the role assigned to profitability as a criterion for measuring success are all likely to remain as continuing barriers to effective communication. They are part of the continuing tension inherent in a commitment to effective innovation as one aspect of maintaining an effective organization, capable of accommodating to its environment. Awareness of the existence of these barriers can perhaps be reflected in a growing tolerance on the part of the participants in the struggle and recognition of the necessity for conflict and for controversy in expressing points of view, if a viable organization is to be maintained. By the same token, continued exposure over long periods of time does tend to modify the values of each of the major participants in this activity and bring them closer together in their points of view. The long-term viability of the enterprise and effective institutionalization of change require that new proposals for action must survive the crossfire of this adversary process.

Summary

The abundant evidence that R&D is only a peripheral member of the business team despite decades of industrial involvement suggests the existing deep-seated barriers to effective communication. The most obvious of these barriers—the terminology and techniques of science and engineering—is in fact the easiest to reduce. Perceptual barriers are more stubborn because they reflect differences in cognitive and cultural style of the sort considered by Snow[9] and because each party is ignorant of the constraints and pressures under which the other works. Technical people in R&D typically don't appreciate the long list of hurdles to be overcome before an invention becomes an innovation. People in operations don't appreciate the personal uncertainty inherent in creative technical work, where years of effort may come to naught.

Most intractable are the value barriers created by fundamental differences in life style, such as ascribing meaning to the passage of time and in using time to measure progress. Differences in the relative worth of achieving action versus increasing knowledge also represent a communication barrier. Differing standards for evaluating personal success further complicate the problem of communications. These barriers are deeply rooted in perceptions and behavior, and therefore it is not surprising that R&D has been slow in gaining acceptance on the business team. Growing sophistication on both sides, as well as extensive exposure to each other's problems and point of view, are gradually improving intercommunication.

14

On Being a Manager

Most management studies focus on the cognitive aspects of the work of management. They examine and analyze those managerial functions that lend themselves to systematic, rational treatment. This emphasis is quite appropriate because much of the work of a manager does in fact lend itself to cognitive processes, and without highly developed cognitive skills no manager can be successful. On the other hand, as most managers are all too well aware, many of their problems do not lend themselves to cognitive techniques—the kinds of things that keep them awake nights frequently seem to defy such analysis. The key feature of this situation is, of course, the fact that the manager himself is a part of the problem. Much of what he does involves interacting with other people, who are the principal sources of the information on which he bases decisions and are the principal vehicles by which he attempts to take action. Consequently, his skill in interacting with people and his perception of his own relationships with people are key ingredients in his success and in his freedom from anxiety. Thus, it is not enough to look at management through the eyes of the manager alone; rather, one must find ways to put the manager in the picture himself. What roles does he play in the scheme of things?

There is, of course, a body of literature and a field of practice devoted to managerial techniques and personnel management. While it goes by a variety of names, it is in one way or another associated with improving interpersonal relationships. This body of literature also has an important place in improving managerial skills. It focuses on the manager as an individual. It seeks to sharpen his skills and to improve his perceptions of his own relationships with people in any situation. The important point is, however, that the manager isn't an individual in just any kind of situation. He is a manager at a particular location, at a particular point in time, with a particular group of people reporting to him, with certain expectations placed upon him by virtue of his location in this multidimensional framework.

Consequently, we are not examining an unstructured interpersonal relationship; we are looking at a stylized interaction between a manager and those in his group. The demands that the organization places on the manager with respect to behavior he should exhibit and to work he should accomplish, as well as the expectations of the people in his group with respect to what he should do and how he should behave, are key ingredients in determining the forces that impinge upon him, either intermittently or constantly. These forces help to define his problem, to establish the constraints within which he must operate, and also to provide the resources and mechanisms by which he can be effective.

Thus, the manager finds himself forced to play many roles, and his perception of these roles and of the timing required to change from one role to another will be very important factors in his success. One would not argue, of course, that these roles exist completely independently of the cognitive work of managing, which involves analyzing problems, gathering facts, evaluating risks, seeking optima, making effective trade-offs, choosing courses of action, and laying out schedules for accomplishment. These generalized cognitive features of the work of the manager are carried out in a variety of circumstances where he is playing different roles, and his awareness of the role that is appropriate to the occasion is absolutely crucial to his success.

Group Appraisal

In this chapter I should like to examine a variety of these roles and their impact on the work of the manager. First I'd like to reverse the normal view of him. Instead of looking at the world from behind his desk, let us look at him first through the eyes of the people in his group. What is his role from their point of view? What do they expect of him? In short, what's the boss for? After hundreds of interviews and many more hundreds of conversations with technical people regarding their work, the environment in which they operate, and their attitudes toward management, some interesting perspectives have emerged regarding their perception of the role of the boss in their lives.

These views are interesting for the material that they ignore or minimize, as well as for the aspects they emphasize. First, we must question what is perhaps the most common assumption, particularly with regard to technical management, that the work of a manager is focused on the technical aspects of the job. Viewed superficially, it is commonly assumed that the technical manager's role is to provide technical leadership, to establish technical objectives, and to provide the key technical knowledge with respect to the work of the R & D organization. This assumption simply is not borne out by the assertions of technical people in R & D organizations. When asked in unstructured circumstances to elaborate on their perception of what the boss is there for, very scant attention was paid to his role as a technical leader. As a matter of fact, in many cases people went out of their way to deny this feature of his role.

Since even in the relatively nonauthoritarian atmosphere of a technical organization a manager is a significant power figure in the lives of those in his group, it is likely that he is a person about whom they feel some ambivalence. Both from the negative comments provided as well as the potentially attractive aspects of a manager's job which were omitted from the discussion, one could easily conclude that good technical people see more undesirable than attractive features in a manager's job. The fact that very competent technical people do accept managerial positions indicates that this is not an accurate reflection of their feelings. Consequently, while the comments described below may be accepted as true, they are not the whole truth. The selective filter on feelings which their incompleteness reflects is in itself a valuable insight for the effective manager to keep in mind.

Critic

One of the striking features of these conversations is that in spite of the fact that the focus is on analysis of the technical managerial role, the terminology of the performing arts represents a surprisingly useful way to describe the reactions and observations that people in the survey provided.

Thus, the principal role that technical people ascribed to the manager is that of critic, used in a sense analogous to its use in the performing arts. They recognize that their work must indeed be evaluated, that somebody must be able to judge the professional adequacy, the technical relevance of what they are doing in relation to the needs of the organization. They describe this as the first and foremost responsibility of their manager, as seen through their eyes. Naturally, it is one to which they attribute great importance. In view of the fact that the work of most organizations covers a variety of technical fields and the level of worldwide technical activity is high, they regard the work of a manager's being technical critic as virtually a full-time job. They feel that the requirement to maintain sufficient cognizance of the state-of-the-art in a variety of fields, so as to be able to make valid judgments that adequately reflect the current state-of-the-art, is an exceedingly challenging intellectual task. It requires both the full energy and virtually the full-time resources of the manager to complete satisfactorily.

A distinction is drawn between this work and providing technical leadership. As a matter of fact, although the term is awkward, one might label this managerial role as "technical followership." Technical people view this requirement as one to understand (after the fact) what they have done and to appreciate the subtleties and the sophistication of the ideas and techniques that they've employed as an exceedingly demanding one. And they are quite upset when they believe that their manager is not up to the task, since in a very real sense they recognize that their lives are in his hands. To the extent that he is incapable of making sound judgments, does not perceive the niceties of what they are doing, cannot relate their output to the needs of the organization, their own careers will suffer. Therefore, they feel he has a strong ethical obligation to be able to perform this work satisfactorily and to devote all the time that is necessary to insure that their own accomplishments are competently judged and their own careers protected.

Note that this point of view with respect to judging performance is in sharp contrast to the circumstances with respect to judging performance in a university, the other principal organization in which R & D is performed. In a university, performance is judged by peers in a collegial framework. In principle at least, the judgment is collective, impersonal, and only partially related to direct contribution to the university itself. A power figure equivalent to a manager may appear on the scene, but he is not a formal part of the institutional framework and he is usually less visible.

Mature technical people describe a sort of metamorphosis that they undergo as they reach maturity in their technical work. They indicate that as they started their technical careers, they tended to view their first boss very much in the same light that they had viewed professors at college. He was regarded as the man to whom they should look for guidance and inspiration. As they achieved some success in their technical work and began to establish a sense of their own identity as full-fledged technical professionals—able to carry their own weight, able to make their own decisions, and able to perceive their own problems and opportunities—they found it necessary to modify their view of the manager as a "father" figure who provided technical guidance and inspiration. This view was incompatible with their emerging view of themselves as mature technical people. Furthermore, as they gained experience they acquired a new insight into the operation of the group and the limitations on the manager's ability and time. They felt that not only was it frequently impossible for him to provide technical leadership for the variety of technical work within his purview (he simply couldn't know enough), but also it would be ineffective management to attempt to do so. He would not be making good use of the talents available in his group. Consequently, they believed the effective manager would not seek to provide technical leadership, but rather would draw forth the talents of his senior technical people and thus multiply the total technical leadership available to the operation. Thus, mature technical professionals go from a period in which they view the manager as a "Herr professor," providing inspiration and guidance, to a point of view in which they see the manager as one who stands on the sidelines and elicits technical leadership from the mature people in the organization.

Agent

The second role that technical people ascribe to their managers is that of agent, and again the analogy to the performing arts is apt. Indeed, people frequently use the specific term "agent" in describing the role of their manager. They view his job as selling their capabilities and outputs to prospective clients, whether they be higher levels of management in the organization or outside clients who are prospective contractors. These technical people recognize that many of the decisions that involve the future of the organization, that involve their own future, will be made at meetings at which they are not present. In these meetings the work they are undertaking will be represented by their manager. To the extent that he can do it with skill, vigor, and enthusiasm, and to the extent that he can project an exciting vision of what is possible to the prospective clients and thus elicit their support, the organization will receive support and in turn the individual will have his own work supported. To the extent that the manager fails to do this job satisfactorily, the individual will find himself handicapped. What is worse, there is little he can do about it because he will not be present when these decisions are made.

In this area, as in the role of critic, the technical people see their manager as requiring a high order of technical skill in order to be successful. Whether or not it is fair, in many cases technical people ascribe a manager's refusal to support their work to his own fear of incompetence. They believe that when pinned to the wall by hostile or unbelieving clients or higher management, he would lack sufficient technical understanding to provide adequate justification and support for the work. This leads him to avoid the risk by turning the work off himself. As I indicated, this view may be unfair, but it is an excuse frequently advanced by technical people for explaining why their manager has chosen not to support their ideas.

Again, technical people see the manager as having a strong ethical obligation to be an effective agent, since to the extent that he succeeds, their futures will be secured and protected or, conversely, their careers will be damaged and there will be very little that they can do about it. Once again the individual is essentially in the hands of his manager. In addition to needing highly technical skills, a manager also needs effective skills as a salesman for the work of the organization. Technical people are frequently uncomfortable at the prospect of having to participate in a sales effort and prefer to feel that good work will sell itself, but they are also realists. They know that the merits and potential opportunities generated by a technical program have to be explained and made to seem important and workable on an investment basis. They are profoundly grateful for people who are skilled at the task.

Producer

The third role of the manager might well be termed that of producer, or the individual who both supplies the resources and molds the resources of the organization to the task at hand. In this role, technical people ascribe less importance to professional technical skill and more importance to the traits of toughness, shrewdness, and skill in political in-fighting. They are aware that there is a budget, which must in some fashion be divided up among the competing units of the organization. They view this as an essentially political process in which people maneuver for position and fight for advantage. If their manager is successful in this political in-fighting, they will get at least their proportionate share of the budget, they will have the space they need, and they will have the resources for replenishing facilities. If he is unsuccessful, no matter how good he may be technically, the group will fail because it will not have the resources to carry out its ideas and complete its programs.

Interestingly enough, skill in this area can provide adequate cover for deficiencies in a variety of other areas. Technical people are willing to put up with quite a lot in the way of managerial inadequacies, provided the manager obtains the resources that they need to complete their work and enables them to achieve success as individuals, whether or not the manager himself will recognize and give the reward that they believe is their due. What they tend to develop is a sort of cynicism toward the work of the organization, which leads them to insure that in one way or another their own capability and their own outputs are recognized in the outside world. If necessary, they can then circumvent the failure of the manager to recognize the value of their contributions, even if it means severing their relationship with the organization in order to capitalize on their enhanced reputation.

Stage Hand

To complete our analogies with the performing arts, the fourth role of the manager might, without too much stretching, be termed the "stage hand." Technical people are aware of the fact that there are a variety of tasks associated with the operation of the organization which they regard as somewhere between trivial and irritating. Letters must be answered, clients' ruffled feathers must be smoothed, relationships with sister organizations must be maintained, laggards must be prodded to maintain schedules, contract proposals must be written. All of the "busy" work required to make an organization run smoothly must be performed by somebody. They view with amazement the manager's willingness to tackle such tasks, and they are simply grateful for his keeping it off their backs. In discussing such work, they frequently comment that the technical world has lost a good technical man in return for one who is now just a "paper shuffler." This term is used over and over again by technical people to describe with regret the transfer of a man from individual technical work to management.

Common Themes

A number of general comments should be made about the observations that people made about their managers in these interviews. The first is to emphasize something that has already been mentioned—the strong ethical element that technical people ascribe to the work of management. They see that in many ways their professional careers are quite literally in the hands of their manager. This concern has nothing to do with integrity. It is fundamentally a matter of competence. To the extent that the manager is competent in making sound technical judgments regarding the significance of an individual's accomplishments, is skilled in perceiving the relevance of work to the needs of the organization, and is skilled in selling the work to outside clients, the individual will himself prosper and benefit. To the extent that the manager fails, the individual's career will be blighted or badly damaged and there is practically nothing he can do about it except get out of the organization. Thus, the ethical responsibility of a manager to be competent and effective looms large in these interviews.

A second observation is to point out that all previous analogies to the performing arts avoided any suggestion of the manager's being on stage. The stars of the show, the people who actually perform the work of research and development, are the technical people. The manager is seen as off stage in the wings, being helpful in a variety of ways while the technical people are the stars on stage. Although most managers would deny this belief when asked, their participation in decision making on programs and resources, and their extensive access to information, may in all too many cases lead them to regard themselves as the stars of the show. This view is clearly not consistent with the view of the technical group members, who see the generation of creative ideas as being the truly demanding tasks to which the work of management is subordinated.

A third observation has to do with the strong need of technical people —and undoubtedly of all people—for a large degree of predictability in their work universe. It is important for the manager to declare himself as an understanding, reasonable human being. It is important for him to let the people in his group know what he is like, to know what he stands for, to know his goals, to know his criteria for measuring performance. Only by so doing does he give them the tools needed to establish some order in their work universe and to insure that they have some understanding of the nature of the decisions to expect from him. It is quite apparent that disorder, or a lack of predictability, generates a high degree of anxiety in people. If they believe their boss to be unpredictable, that his behavior is random, he becomes a major problem in the organization. Consequently, when he declares himself, the manager may run the risk of failing to live up to his own standards and therefore of being vulnerable to criticism and ridicule. If he neglects this declaration of principles, he diverts resources, which otherwise could be used for productive tasks, to the work of trying to "figure him out." It is a matter of critical concern for people to understand what their manager wants and how he is likely to respond to a given situation. Then, if he should make the task difficult, they will simply devote more energy and effort to it. Neurotic behavior is sometimes described as being an inability to interpret incoming information from the world around us, and in this sense an unpredictable manager can create a neurotic organization.

Institutionally Imposed Managerial Roles

Having examined the roles the technical people assign their manager, we now switch our attention to look at the roles the organization or the institution imposes on the manager. Thus, we are now looking at the manager through the eyes of his peers and his superiors in the organization. These roles should be distinguished from the functional differences in management. Depending on where a manager is located in the organization and the problems of the organization at the time, he may find himself having to perform quite different roles, irrespective of the functional assignment; and, of course, at higher organizational levels managerial assignments tend to be multifunctional.

These various roles are intertwined and to some extent they are all a part of managerial work, but they vary in proportion quite substantially from one position to another, and a manager's perceptiveness in recognizing the role requirements of the immediate situation will have a lot to do with his being successful. Furthermore, in terms of individual capabilities, managers are typically much better at some managerial roles than others. There-fore, they might be wise to seek only those managerial situations in which the roles at which they are skilled are dominant, or at least they should avoid overstraining their capacity to develop additional role skills. The reader will recognize that these role descriptions are somewhat idealized in order to call attention to their salient features.

Achiever

The first role of the manager is that of "achiever." This is generally the attribute first looked for in seeking fledgling managers—the ability to get things done. The term "achiever" has been used deliberately in place of the more commonly used quality of "leadership" because there are in fact two important distinguishing features of the achiever role. The first is the energy and drive associated with being a leader—the ability to maintain sustained effort, to take charge of a situation. This drive for power or dominance is a frequently recognized attribute of managerial success. On the other hand, in order to be an achiever such drive must be coupled with another ingredient, equally important and equally scarce—the ability to maintain focus, to stay goal-oriented, to keep things in perspective as one pursues the task(s) at hand. While the requirement to be an achiever is a feature of every managerial job, it is the dominant feature of much of project and program management in which the goal is laid out and the task is to drive toward that goal as effectively and vigorously as possible. The role of the manager in this situation is to marshal, mold, and focus the resources necessary to achieve the goal in minimum time and at minimum cost to the sponsor. Some managers are superb at precisely this task, but they are not necessarily equally gifted in other managerial roles. Consequently, it might be wise for them to seek only achiever roles in which the drive for accom-plishment is a significant factor in the role of the manager.

Advocate / Salesman

The next institutional role of the manager is that of "advocate/salesman," analogous to the "agent" role noted earlier. This is frequently dominant in the first-level management jobs of the organization. The distinguishing feature of this managerial role is directly due to the fact that the time scale for measurement of accomplishment is so short that the manager has very limited opportunity to alter his resources. In other words, he has a small group, or is required to assemble a small group, as rapidly as possible. This time demand permits him to do little other than use the talents available in whatever way will most effectively serve the needs of the organization. He frequently does not have time to modify the resources significantly in order to seek some different, perhaps more attractive, goal. Thus, his success will be measured very largely by the extent to which he manages to find tasks that the resources of his small group are able to accomplish satisfactorily and to make these tasks at least appear relevant to the needs of the organization.

As a result, not surprisingly, he finds himself almost obsessed with the requirement to sell the resources of his group, to find tasks that it is able to perform, and to become an advocate for the validity and necessity of these tasks to meet the needs of the organization. Time and circumstances dictate that to a first approximation he must make do with what he has, and his survival will depend on his making what he is able to do seem necessary and desirable from the organization's point of view. Again, the role of advocate/salesman is to some extent a feature of many, if not most, managerial jobs. On the other hand, it is the dominant feature of certain managerial jobs and particularly of first-level technical positions. Some people are superbly skilled at sizing up their group, recognizing its key talents, and finding ways to make these talents serve the needs of the organization in a very effective fashion.

Resource Allocator

The third institutional role that a manager must play is that of resource allocator. It is interesting that technical people rarely volunteer information on this aspect of their manager's work. It is possible that the subject generates anxiety and thus is one they tend to suppress. Resource allocation becomes increasingly important as one moves to higher levels in the organization. The skills and talents required for this role are very different from those of either achiever or advocate/salesman. First of all, a somewhat longer time scale for the measurement of accomplishment is usually involved. This has the effect of providing opportunity for the manager to modify his resources to some extent in order to achieve an optimum contribution to the organization as a whole.

Given the opportunity to modify resources, the manager now has the requirement to evaluate relative opportunities and relative risks in relation to both present and potential capabilities. He must balance resources as he modifies them to seek an optimum in both the makeup of capabilities and the allocation of resources among competing opportunities. In this situation, the advocate/salesman is unlikely to act perceptively. The requirement is not to grab a goal in order to go plunging ahead, but rather to use discretion, judgment, and patience in deciding the proper course of action and in balancing resources so that perhaps others can then plunge ahead on the tasks chosen to be done.

A resource allocator role calls for quite different skills on the part of the manager. In many cases it calls for skills for which his past experience has not provided adequate preparation. Heretofore the manager has been relying principally on his own technical knowledge and first-hand experience in dealing with the work to be done. Growing out of this direct first-hand experience is a highly honed intuition, which gives him the skills to weigh probabilities for success. But now he is operating in a larger framework where much of the information comes to him in the form of abstractions and from areas of work with which he does not have first-hand experience. Thus, he is suddenly confronted with the task of making judgments in areas where his own knowledge appears inadequate. And for the first time he encounters a kind of managerial anxiety with which he will have to live from now on. He will now be working with information provided by other people from areas where he lacks first-hand experience.

One of the manager's principal contributions as a resource allocator will be the judgments he makes of people and of the validity of the information they present to him. Some managers are simply unable to perform this task satisfactorily, unable to develop the conceptual tools to deal with information in abstract form, and—perhaps even more important—they are unable to tolerate the anxiety that is inherent in making judgments and in operating in an environment permeated with a high level of ambiguity. Their response may be a neurotic demand for still more information, but, in terms of reducing anxiety and improving managerial decisiveness, acceding to this demand will likely prove dysfunctional. It will increase anxiety, not reduce it.

Goal Setter

The final role that the institution imposes on the manager is that of goal setter. This role is obviously most dominant in the job of the chief executive or the head of any major component in the organization. But, again to some extent, it is inherent in all managerial work. In this role the manager is dealing with the diffuse fundamental problems involved in affirming the basic purposes of the organization itself. He must absorb and put in perspective the external world in which the organization functions. He must look at the resources within the organization and realistically appraise its capability for modifying those resources in timely fashion. Then he must look at himself and decide what he seeks in terms of contribution to life and to society. From these disparate inputs he must try to integrate a purpose for the organization as a whole during his term in office. To the extent that he does this job well and develops the confidence and self-reliance to remain steadfast in the face of uncertainty and hardship, the organization will maintain a sense of purpose and of continuity. To the extent that he is unable to do it, or, more important, to the extent that he is unable to maintain steadfastness in the pursuit of his objectives, the organization will lack purpose and will not come into focus.

It is not surprising that the heads of organizations become fascinated with history, particularly the history of their own organization, because in this history they hope to find clues that will guide them in establishing or in modifying the basic purposes of the organization. There are no objective rigorous standards that will evaluate one set of purposes or goals as inherently superior to another. The key ingredient is the confidence of the manager in making the judgment, his belief in the rightness and attainability of the goals he sets, and his willingness to dedicate himself and the organization to the pursuit of these goals.

It is widely recognized that quite different styles can be pursued successfully and that widely different objectives can be achieved by major industrial firms. The critical step is to make the commitment. This requires a level of confidence that comes only from deep belief in the rightness of what one is doing. Thus, it is not surprising that the heads of major organizations are very assertive, strong-willed men. If they did not have this capacity for belief in the rightness of what they are doing, they could not make the personal commitment nor could they demand of the organization the commitment that is necessary to achieve major purposes.

Summary

Most studies of management have stressed the personal qualities associated with the drive for power and the cognitive skills required for decision making and planning. This discussion has examined a variety of managerial roles, all of which to varying degrees come into play during a managerial career. The variety of role demands, the repertoire of skills they require, and the perception and flexibility needed to switch roles clearly exceed the capacity of most (possibly all) managers. This discussion is intended to help replace intuitive grasp with conceptual understanding and thus hopefully to expand managerial capacity.

Among the chief talents a manager needs are the ability to sort out the various role requirements that are implicit in each specific managerial assignment, the skill to play each role acceptably (or to surround himself with people who can compensate for his deficiencies), and the capability to absorb the distress resulting from being forced to fulfill incompatible roles. The demands of the organization for accomplishment and for decisions regarding allocation of resources must be accommodated in some fashion with the demands of technical people for autonomy, for support of their work, and for a starring role in their technical assignments. These latter demands are probably no different in kind from those of most members of an organization, but an R & D organization is almost unique in its dependence on the creative dedication of the staff.

Thus, an R & D manager needs unusual skill in mediating these role demands. Perhaps his most difficult task is to keep himself in perspective. Because of his participation in planning, communicating, and decision making, he quite naturally comes to regard himself as a central actor in R & D. It is hard to remember that his people—especially his best people—have a different perception. Equally important throughout his career is his ability to perceive the differing role demands of new managerial positions. I have known some superb first-line technical managers who were poorly equipped to allocate resources and didn't even perceive the requirement for their boss to do so. Temporary assignments of the type we will be discussing in Chapter 15 can help broaden the manager's repertoire of role skills.

15 Managing Temporary Organizations

When one considers the amount of attention paid to forecasting the future in many different areas, the future of large organizations and of their management has received surprisingly little attention. One common theme that emerges from the limited amount of work done is the assumption that a significant future characteristic of large industrial organizations—and probably large organizations of any sort—will be an increasing fluidity in their internal mode of operation. A major portion of their work will be accomplished by temporary teams that are formed for specific purposes. These teams will generally be composed of people taken from various parts of the organization, brought together for the particular task, and then presumably disbanded and returned to their permanent locations.

Thus, as futurists see the situation, it is likely that large organizations will become a mixture of more or less permanent assignments interspersed with, and perhaps underlying, a kaleidoscope of temporary assignments such as projects, task forces, or study teams, which are created temporarily for specific work and then disbanded once the work is completed.

On the whole, the consideration that has been given this subject is superficial. Only general comments have been made about the overall character of such temporary organizations. Little systematic and careful attention has been given to exactly how they would function. Even more important, the viewpoint adopted in making these predictions about the future is essentially macroscopic—it looks at the entire organization. Little or no consideration has been given to a microscopic examination of the

problem of managing such temporary organizations. Since the entire concept will live or die depending on the effectiveness of this mode of operation, study of the problems of managing temporary organizations seems to
be in order.

As noted early in this book one of the attractive features of the management of R & D as an area for study is the extent to which R & D
management experience may be a leading indicator of management problems that will be faced in other aspects of industrial management. Research
and development is in a particularly advantageous position with respect to
accumulated experience in the functioning of temporary organizations. It is
perhaps inevitable that in an activity devoted to the creation of change, the
patterns of organization would exhibit a considerable degree of fluidity and
temporariness. For whatever reason, temporary groups created to prepare
proposals, evaluate problems or opportunities and propose solutions, resolve crises, develop prototypes or new designs, etc., are a way of life in R
& D. Despite the prevalence of this mode of operation, the observation
regarding the lack of systematic studies of the management of temporary
organizations applies with equal force to R & D. This chapter explores the
special problems created by virtue of the temporary character of an organization, especially with regard to the kinds of people typically assigned to it,
the work process that generates its output, and the special demands made of
its manager.

Characteristics of Temporary Assignments

Studies of the work of management rarely take *time* into account as a
specific element of the environment. This omission was discussed in Chapter 4. It is likely that neglect of this element is more or less by default
because the implicit assumption is made that the manager is operating in a
time frame that is sufficiently long so that it can be ignored for purposes of
analyzing the nature of his work. What if that isn't true? We are then
concerned with a much more restricted "here and now" view of time. What
are the implications of a situation in which the life of the organization itself
is a major consideration in determining the character of its work, in the
sense that its existence is sufficiently short that (1) the specification of the
work that can be accomplished within the allowed time is in itself a major
part of the challenge of the task at hand; and (2) the imminent termination of

the organization is a major factor in the working environment? It is likely that an assignment to manage in such circumstances will in the best of cases impose in more critical form and perhaps with greater urgency the problems that one ordinarily encounters in management. At worst, it is possible that entirely new problems will be created by the special characteristics of such a temporary organization.

The following discussion should be regarded as a tentative probe into this new area of the time imperative. It is based on an attempt to codify extensive experience in, and observation of, many temporary organizations in R & D. It is probable, although not yet demonstrated, that these same features are characteristic of other temporary organizations as well.

Defining a Temporary Organization

What is a temporary organization? In starting this analysis it is necessary to establish some boundaries because a large variety of temporary organizations will undoubtedly be created in the future operation of large corporations, and it is therefore necessary to specify the type from which this analysis is drawn. The temporary organization under consideration here has three significant characteristics. The first is the nature of its objective. The organization I have in mind may be regarded essentially as a "one-act-play." A specific task is assigned. This task frequently will involve a paperwork output in terms of a study or appraisal recommending a plan of action on a technical problem or preparing a contract proposal. In some cases it may involve the preparation of prototype hardware or the accomplishment of technology transfer. It has many similarities to a project organization that typically has a single goal to achieve, at the end of which the people manning the project will seek employment elsewhere. In most cases, because of the specific convergent nature of the assignment, the objective is put on a "best effort" basis; i.e., within an allotted time the people assigned to the task will produce the best result of which they are capable. Sometimes the sponsor has no clear idea of the results he wants. In any event, there will not be time to iterate to more effective conclusions or to go back and change work in the light of additional experience.

The second characteristic, not unexpectedly, is that the organization operates in a specified and limited time frame—by such and such a date a task will be completed. No extension of time will be permitted, and thus time becomes a dominant factor in determining how much work can be done; in effect, performance goals are scaled to fit the time available. In some cases the time scale is simply specified as requiring the accomplishment of a specific assignment as rapidly as possible, without indicating the due date for completion.

The third characteristic of these temporary organizations involves the unusual character of the staff. The people typically come from a variety of locations throughout the larger parent organization. They are assigned on a temporary basis, which may be part-time work scattered over several months or full-time work for a shorter period of time. The important thing is that the workers must have permanent assignment elsewhere in the parent organization. Hopefully, they are put on this task because they possess specialized skills that are regarded as important to the completion of the work. (They might also be put on the task because they are regarded as dispensable by their parent component!) However, their own career assignments are in other parts of the organization and their own aspirations for advancement or increased stature are focused on the more permanent structure that exists elsewhere in the total organization.

Furthermore, these people not infrequently come from a variety of assignments in the larger organization. They represent different ages, levels of experience, and levels of responsibility. They constitute a veritable menagerie of interests, skills, and points of view. The initial status structure of the temporary group could be described as chaotic. It has no coherent hierarchy. The people thrown into the melting pot come from different statuses in their permanent assignments; they have differing expectations of how to be treated in this temporary organization, and of how much influence and control they should have over its operation. In addition, their initial commitment to the task of the temporary organization is at best uncertain. In many cases their understanding of why the task is being performed or why they were chosen to participate is quite limited. Their own commitment to the success of the operation has yet to be created, and in many cases they come to the operation with what could be termed a hidden agenda: They hope the group will eventually accomplish selected goals that will redound to their advantage or to the advantage of the permanent group that they believe they represent in the formation of the temporary organization. These hidden agendas or implicit objectives may or may not be destructive to the work of the group, but they must gradually be identified—at least covertly—and reconciled with the work of the group.

Finally, these people in many cases are powerful personalities who have had little recent experience in working in groups of any sort and particularly in special task forces. They have never worked together as a unit, and no group pattern of behavior has been established. They frequently come into the operation as managers who are accustomed to functioning in a managerial capacity, dealing with subordinates rather than acting as equals in a large, rather amorphous peer group.

Defining Objectives

Not surprisingly under these circumstances, the work of a temporary organization is an anxiety-ridden, tension-filled, physically exhausting activity. The group is operating in real time, sometimes in accelerated real time, where the completion of the task in the prescribed time is in itself perhaps the most challenging aspect of the work to be done. Under these conditions the manner in which the group goes about its work is crucial to its success. The first requirement obviously is to define the task that the group will seek to accomplish. In almost every case the group starts out with an assignment from a sponsoring individual or sponsoring organization, but rarely is this assignment sufficient in detail or generality to serve adequately as a specification for the work of the group. Thus, almost immediately, the group faces a threefold task in defining its work.

First, what does the sponsor really want? Does the given assignment appropriately define what is desired? If one looked more carefully or talked with additional people, would he discover that there were nuances to the assignment that are not now apparent? How does the group insure that it knows what is wanted? Closely related is likely to be an ongoing argument among the members of the group as to whether or not its task is to give the sponsor what he wants or whether it should look at the situation as dispassionately and objectively as possible and arrive at what it regards as the best solution to the problem at hand, irrespective of the intentions or desires of the sponsor. In other words, will its solution be work-oriented or politically oriented? Throughout its work the group will encounter a persistent concern over the credibility of its final output, and will struggle with the problem of balancing political considerations, which may affect the credibility of the result, against work-oriented criteria, which will determine its intrinsic value. The third element of this ongoing task of defining the work of the group is: What is in fact accomplishable in the time available? Given the constraints under which the group is operating with respect to time, manpower, and access to information, how much work can it promise and deliver?

One aspect of this situation which becomes immediately obvious is that the process of defining objectives is iterative. In spite of the fact that the group begins to address this problem almost immediately upon being assembled and seeks to determine a course of action, in almost no case is this course of action an adequate description to guide its work from that time forth. Rather it must go back again and again to reexamine its specification of what is accomplishable, and must redefine the balance of work in the context of work-oriented versus political considerations. In effect, this process continues until the group runs out of time and finally adopts the most expedient solution obtainable within the remaining time.

Designating Methodology

Having arrived at a tentative working statement of the mission of the temporary organization, the next task of the group is to develop the methodology and the information to be used in accomplishing its work. The first requirement is to specify in much more detail exactly what work has to be done in order to carry out the mission. This work is typically delineated and assigned so as to take advantage of the specialized talents of the members of the group. Because of the severe limits of time, there is a strong bias in favor of applying as much as possible of the methodology and information already available. Failing that, the group resorts to available methodology and adapts it to the work to be done. The ultimate recourse is to undertake the invention of the methodology that will be required to complete the work.

While the inexorable pressure of time creates a strong bias toward using available techniques, sad experience demonstrates that there is essentially no such thing as an adequate set of instructions for use by the uninitiated in applying available technology. Consequently, considerable frustrating time is required for the group to become familiar with the potentially applicable methodology and to identify that which is useful by trial and error. This frustrating process frequently generates a great deal of anxiety and even hostility on the part of the group as it struggles with the task. No matter what has been done in the past under other circumstances, this particular group facing its special problem must learn to make the applicable methodology its own for the task at hand. Despite its frustration and the feeling that time is fleeting, with little accomplished, the temporary group must go through this induction process.

As time passes, there will be increasing awareness that the group will have to make do with what tools it has been able to develop; it cannot afford to go back and refine methodology. It cannot discard methods that turn out to be less than ideal. It must use the tools available to arrive at the best solution possible under the circumstances. The discipline required to face up to this problem is one of the more difficult tasks that the group has, particularly among those people who are strongly oriented toward the irreplaceability of rigorous logical thinking and systematic approaches to problems. Their standards of intellectual excellence are insulted by the requirements to use what they regard as sloppy techniques or inexact measures, simply because there is no time to accomplish the work more rigorously and elegantly.

Inevitably in almost every group there are people who worry about the validity of the information and methodology to be applied. They continually create straw men, which the group must dispose of. To some extent their contribution is important because it provides a continuing scrutiny of the methodological soundness and rigor of the thinking of the group. On the other hand, it is frustrating to others in the group because it is time consuming and causes them to diverge from the more important work of completing the task at hand. Many of the real problems that the group must address can be perceived and dealt with only by getting on with the work rather than thinking about it or talking about it.

Having completed, at least on a temporary basis, the work of specifying the methodology that will be used, the next task is to assign specific responsibility to people to carry out portions of the work. This assignment typically reflects the varied skills of the members of the group, but it also may have to reflect the political interests of the various factions potentially affected by the output of the group's work. And then, finally, all work must be assembled in a final output—be it report, prototype, or final design —that has sufficient integration and coherence to provide its own credibility in terms of its impact on the potential client or sponsor. This final stage again requires that the group reach a consensus by some means or another, and the manner by which it is done is one of the things with which the group must struggle. Usually there is not sufficient time to talk through and solve all problems. In some cases the chairman, some other individual, or an alignment of power in the group must essentially force a conclusion and resolve conflict, not necessarily in the most desirable fashion but in a way that recognizes the inexorable imperatives of the time scale in which the work is being conducted.

Process Dynamics

In addition to the output-oriented aspect of the work of the group, which involves the accomplishment of its specific task, there is another crucial aspect, which one might call "process dynamics." Members of the group somehow or another have to learn to work together. Here one faces in heightened form many of the classical features of group interactions, heightened primarily because of the shortened time scale and the requirement to achieve specific goals under considerable pressure. As noted earlier, these people are likely to have never worked together as a group. Many of them may have had little experience in participating in group activities.

The first thing to establish is the interaction mode. How will conversation occur in the group? How will people be recognized? What sorts of rules will the group adopt to govern its deliberations, its scheduling of the time of meetings, the length of meetings, the subject matter of meetings—all the things that have to do with how the group will go about accomplishing its task? The leader or manager of the group may provide some suggestions or a schedule for this kind of activity, but primarily it involves a joint learning activity on the part of all the people. There is much probing among members to uncover strengths and weaknesses, to identify individual modes of operation, to discover how best to approach people in order to be effective with them. Much time will inevitably be devoted to this task while the group goes about the extrinsic function of completing its work.

Two kinds of role specializations ordinarily emerge out of this activity in process dynamics. One involves the particular technical specialty of each individual which led to his being asked to serve in the first place. Here —unless his capability has been unduly inflated—he is accepted as the group's expert in his field and goes relatively unchallenged. He is in fact sought out for the inputs that the group will need in this area. Quite apart from these functional expert roles are the new roles that also have to emerge with respect to the functioning of the group itself. Some of these roles involve providing the methodological tools the group will need for its tasks and which have to be invented or rediscovered by the group itself. These methodological tools are not created or adapted by the entire group, but rather by certain people who are discovered to be more skilled in this kind of activity. This role assignment is difficult to anticipate in advance and has little connection with functional expertise.

Another role is that of critics; i.e., those who persistently question the methodological soundness of the approaches being used and who criticize the level of rigor in the group's thinking. Additional crucial roles are played by those who act as integrators and synthesizers, pulling together the sometimes disparate and desultory discussions of the group and finding the common thread that enables the group to proceed productively with its work. One important role is that of the disciplinarian, who somehow or another cuts off the people who are taking the group down unproductive or trivial paths or who are unduly delaying progress. A final crucial role is that of the peacemaker who helps to calm tempers and provides the bit of humor needed on occasion to help the group overcome the hostility and anxiety it generates in the course of doing its work. This role system emerges spontaneously and is not necessarily a permanent assignment. Different people may play multiple roles at different times in the course of the group's work.

Growing out of role specialization is the gradual emergence of the group's status system. This status system will include the manager or the leader of the group itself, who will also come to be perceived as having a variety of roles, not necessarily always associated with his performing his leadership role. As a matter of fact, the designated leader may even end up not being the de facto leader of the group. The distinctive feature of these temporary organizations is that, irrespective of the statuses of the individuals when in their permanent environment, the operation of this group is a "here and now" proposition in which the statuses within the group result from the effectiveness of the people within this particular circumstance. This sometimes comes as a bit of a shock to people who come to the group with certain expectations with respect to how they will be treated, how much deference they will be shown, and how much influence they will exercise. They find that they have to earn their status anew in this particular circumstance and that the competition may in fact be somewhat different from that occurring in a milieu in which they are dealing with much more familiar material and dealing with people who are experts in a more homogeneous field. By contrast, the people in the group will have heterogeneous backgrounds and all will be operating in unfamiliar territory. The skills permitting effective performance in this milieu are very different from those that lead to success in a stable, relatively familiar environment.

Dealing with Anxiety

The operation of these temporary organizations frequently generates substantial group anxiety. On the one hand, there are the usual problems associated with learning to work in a new group, coming to grips with new people, and learning to be effective and establishing one's place in the hierarchy of a new organization. On the other hand, this normal anxiety is in every case heightened and compounded by the challenging cognitive problem for which the group was created and with which it must deal. In this situation the first thing that usually happens is that the members of the group turn to the manager and demand that he supply clear sailing orders. There is an assumption, either explicit or implicit, that because he is the manager of the group, he knows more about why it was formed and what its objectives are, and more about the nuances and subtleties of the environment in which it will operate than do the other members of the group. Consequently, he is expected to be in a position to give them clear and explicit instructions so that they can get on with the work.

In fact, the group's demand for guidance contains a substantial element of the search for a means to relieve the anxiety generated in the course of coming together. Frequently the leader knows little more than the others about why the group was formed or how it is to function. His lack of sufficient information to provide explicit sailing orders is frequently regarded as a sign of weakness by the rest of the group, and there may be an expression of either overt or covert disappointment that the group isn't receiving very effective leadership. On the other hand, even if the leader does possess adequate information to guide the group, the pressures generated to sort out and establish the process dynamics required for the group to be able to function together, coupled with the unfamiliarity of its task, will effectively block rapid early progress toward the group's objectives.

Concurrent with this early demand for guidance, and closely related to it, is generally an expectation that the leader will provide at least the initial methodological tools for the group to begin its work. Not surprisingly, he is frequently in no position to do so, and even if he is, the group is not yet in a position to make effective use of the tools. Again, the recognition that the leader does not have these tools, that the development of the necessary methodological tools is one of the challenges that the group faces, creates hostility and an expression of disappointment that the leader is not being effective in providing for the needs of the group. This concern over methodology is two-dimensional, with one dimension reflecting objective need and the other representing an attempt to deal with the anxiety that the group is generating. One means frequently devised for dealing with this anxiety is for the group to engage in what one might term "busy work," i.e., extensive efforts to collect data, check the literature, conduct interviews, or make relatively obvious analyses. These projects are undertaken with considerable vigor or enthusiasm, largely because they at least represent something tangible that the group can undertake, leading it to believe that it is indeed making progress and thus helping to relieve its anxiety.

Inevitably in the earlier stages of the group's work, and to some extent throughout its life, there will be a good deal of wheel spinning when the group is not certain what it should do, finds that what it has done is not well conceived, or must go back and retrace its steps. All this effort will be accompanied by a good deal of grumbling that the group is not being effective, that time is being wasted, that the deadline is rapidly approaching, and that somehow or another the group must become more effective.

Unfortunately, this preliminary activity, ineffective though it may seem, is an inevitable feature of initiating a temporary organization. These organizations do in fact have exceedingly difficult problems to cope with; otherwise, they wouldn't have been formed. In most cases the temporary organization must adapt or even invent the methodology that will be used in pursuing its work. It must make a variety of sophisticated and subtle judgments about information that is being developed and about the audience to which the output is to be directed, all of this being accomplished in a very short time scale and being performed by people who hardly know each other. Inevitably the work will involve a number of false starts, and much of what appears to be wasted motion is in fact unavoidable. This situation is rarely accepted with equanimity, but rather tends to exacerbate the relationships within the group.

Repeated experience demonstrates that the group will develop a kind of rhythm and dynamics which, if it can be perceived, will guide the pace of events. Partly the pressure of time forces events but partly the wheel spinning has been more productive than was apparent, especially in helping the process dynamics to emerge. The lost motion diminishes as the group begins to build toward a crescendo and typically the work of the group will be completed in a veritable orgy of activity, with long hours being spent in finally wrestling through to a conclusion and achieving an integrated product.

Juggling Individual and Group Activity

Superimposed on this entire structure is the ongoing problem of the work-a-day procedural activities that fundamentally involve balancing activity at three levels. First is the extent to which the group should seek to achieve its objectives by meeting as a "committee of the whole." This arrangement is recognized on the one hand as frustrating because frequently little seems to be accomplished and, in fact, work done elsewhere frequently is undone at meetings of this sort. On the other hand, there is an overriding recognition that in some way or another the group must come to a consensus, which can be achieved only by meeting together. Consequently, frustrating and time consuming though the meetings may be, a substantial amount of time must be spent on committee-as-a-whole activities in which the group in its entirety wrestles with the problems at hand.

Secondly, there is the work of subcommittees, usually formed to take advantage of specialized skills needed for subtasks. These subcommittees frequently prove most productive in the technical sense of generating the outputs needed. They involve simpler interpersonal relationships and permit more direct time to be devoted to the task at hand, with less effort diverted to process dynamics. However, they also involve the necessity to go back to the full group and to spend considerable time in explaining the work of the subcommittee and in achieving the understanding and concurrence of the group with respect to the work of the subcommittee.

Finally, there is the work of individuals, who frequently find that only in individual activity can they truly come to grips with the problems at hand and thus make their most creative contributions. The total activity of the temporary organization must allow time for each of these three kinds of work, operating in a complicated, interconnected, ad hoc system rather than in orderly sequence. Work will move from individual activity to full group activity, to subcommittee activity and back according to the logic of the moment.

The Managerial Role

What is the manager's role in this exhausting, anxiety-ridden task? To some extent, of course, the role of the manager will be determined by the group because the personalities of the individuals, their backgrounds, and the way in which the group itself emerges as an operating entity will strongly influence the role of the manager. One unusual feature of temporary organizations is that in many cases the manager will not necessarily be of any higher status than the people in the group. In fact, it is not unusual for some members of the group to have higher extrinsic status than does the manager. Consequently, the manager faces the same problem confronting all other members of the group—that of establishing his status and finding his role(s) in the here and now of this intense little society.

Fundamentally, the manager's role in the group will be some combination of four different kinds of roles. The first is that of recording secretary. This is perhaps a minimal role of simply keeping a record of what the group is doing and providing the written report for the group to edit and put in approved form. While this role is essentially a service that the manager can provide for the group, the role of recording secretary can also be a powerful force in driving the group on to action. The man at the blackboard frequently exerts a strong influence on the work of the group by the mere fact of writing down what he selects for recording. By being on his feet when the other people are seated, and by calling attention to the need to return to the schema started on the blackboard, he can impose a kind of managerial discipline on the group no matter what his official function.

The second role, somewhat larger in size, is to act as chairman of the group in the formal sense of this term, i.e., to recognize speakers, to attempt to terminate discussion when it appears to be unproductive or becomes tangential to the objectives of the group, to summarize discussion, etc. This role can be performed not by attempting to contribute significant inputs to the substantive work of the group but rather by focusing effort on providing the interactive structure within which the group can function. If the chairman performs this role vigorously, however, he may curb discussion and lead members of the group to feel that they have not had an opportunity to make their full contribution. This behavior will tend to inhibit the commitment that the members of the group make to its work.

The third role for the manager to attempt is that of a virtuoso, providing most of the key ideas for the group and using the group principally as a backdrop to lend credibility or to provide hands to perform the detailed work needed to demonstrate feasibility. The problems that lead to the creation of temporary organizations rarely lend themselves to this virtuoso approach—they are complex, their ramifications are important, and/or they cut across organizational boundaries. Furthermore, if the manager attempts to advocate his own proposals and competes with the other members of the group from his managerial vantage point, he will strongly inhibit their achieving a sense of commitment to the work. He will frequently find the team members withdrawing, in effect saying: "Well, it's your problem; you solve it." Hence, this role defeats the purpose of setting up the temporary organization in the first place. Nevertheless, the manager will feel strong pressures to perform such a role. He, more than any other member of the team, will be personally identified with the output of the group, and he will have a powerful incentive for the group to be successful. Thus, his personal needs may be counter to the behavior most needed to elicit participation and commitment from the rest of the group.

The final role, and the most productive one, is that of synthesizer—the person who by synthesizing may provide some of the key ideas, ideas which are generated by discussions of the team. He also maintains perspective on the current status and needs of the group. This latter contribution is crucial because of the severe time limits for completing the work. Sophisticated judgments must be made with respect to the amount of time devoted to a given subject and whether or not progress is adequate to permit moving on to the next stage. This is something the manager can provide perhaps better than anybody else in the group, if he has been able to maintain perspective on the results that are possible in the time available.

In carrying out these various roles the manager will find himself faced with some particularly difficult problems. First, he will of necessity be required to absorb a great deal of hostility generated by the group's anxiety. Almost inevitably the group will turn *on* him as well as turn *to* him in its frustration and anxiety because of the time constraints under which it is operating and the uncertainties that the group interaction is generating. If he strikes back and forces the group members to express their hostility elsewhere, they may turn on each other and cause such interpersonal friction that the group may simply never emerge as a coordinated unit. Consequently, one critical service that the manager can provide for the group is to act as an absorber of anxiety that inhibits the work of the group.

His overt recognition that indeed the people do have a difficult problem, and his willingness to accept their criticisms for what they are—reflections of frustration at the inability to get on with the task any faster—can help provide constructive outlets for the group's tensions and permit it to get on with the work at hand more rapidly than it might otherwise do. But absorbing this anxiety imposes a very special strain on the manager.

The second task is more demanding of his managerial talents. He must force the group to reach a conclusion, despite the severe time limits under which it functions. The major problem in accomplishing this task is that the team must arrive at this conclusion despite data that may be inadequate and methodology that may not be sufficiently rigorous and precise to provide the credibility that the group would like. One of the jobs of the manager is to force people to face up to the fact that whether or not they are happy with the responsibility they've been assigned, they have the task of arriving at the best possible conclusion under the circumstances and must not evade that responsibility. In doing this, he must try to make sure that the final output is a group conclusion and not simply his own. This is perhaps the greatest challenge that the manager faces, since only in this way can he realize true commitment from the group, not only to the preparatory work but also to the conclusions that emerge from that work. If he attempts to play the role of the virtuoso or assume full responsibility for the final outcome, he will find that the members of the team are again saying in effect: "It's your problem, your solution. I want no part of it nor do I assume any responsibility for it."

One of the major obstacles that the manager faces in performing his work is the fact that people who serve on these temporary organizations frequently regard themselves as carrying out a very thankless task. Their performance in their permanent position and their permanent managers' evaluation will exercise the principal influence on their future. The manager of the temporary group faces a severe problem in providing adequate incentive and reward for the participants. In most cases no provision is made for these requirements when establishing the temporary organization. The manager does not have control over the salaries of the people. In some cases all he can do is write a letter of appreciation after the work is completed, to insure that at least some record of their contribution and participation is established.

His greatest resource in eliciting participation and commitment is the challenge of the problem assigned the team and the stimulation generated by the caliber of the people assigned to the work. For all concerned, the work represents a departure from the commonplace and an opportunity to work with new people, frequently of high competence. I have heard more than one man comment that serving with one of these temporary organizations was one of the high points of his career. Under these circumstances it is especially important for the manager to avoid the virtuoso role and to foster wide group participation.

It is unfortunate that the inputs of the members of the group inevitably assume a kind of anonymity as far as the final output is concerned and that the relative contribution of the various members will be obscured or blurred by the group identification. Even more unfortunate, the output of the group when the work is complete, is most likely to be associated with the name of its manager. It will be known as "the Smith report," or the "Jones plan," irrespective of his personal contribution. Therefore, it is essential that the manager maintain a low profile and stress the group contribution rather than his own.

Implementing Results

The final aspect of the management of technical organizations for which explicit allowance must be made is in providing for follow-up. The fact that these organizations do have a specific limited objective and a limited life means that more than the normal attention must be given to making effective use of the output of the group. Since it will disband, there will be no continuing organization to provide for implementation. As a rough approximation, it is likely that one-half of the total time available should be devoted to carrying out the initial spadework of generating information and developing the general approach to the problem; one-quarter of the time should be used for driving the group to a conclusion; and then one-quarter of the time should be allowed for follow-up. This task involves first informing and then selling the sponsor with regard to the credibility and validity of the output of the group. While this work is time consuming, it does serve a number of useful purposes. It is an important cross-check on the work of the group itself.

The task of preparing a concise, effective presentation and the interaction generated in seeking the acceptance and implementation of the conclusions by the sponsor is an invaluable discipline for the group. This implementation activity provides an evaluation of whether or not the group has indeed dealt with all aspects of the problem with sufficient sophistication and rigor and whether the appropriate priorities have been selected in reaching conclusions. This interaction with the sponsor not infrequently leads to an improvement in the work of the group. However, unless explicit allowance is made for the time, energy, and effort that will be required to accomplish the follow-up, it is likely that the work of the temporary organization will fail to achieve its potential.

Summary

This discussion of temporary organizations has indicated that participation in such an activity is a different kind of experience. It calls for special skills and it generates special forms of anxiety. If prognoses are correct, participation in temporary organizations will become prevalent, but still it will represent only a small portion of the work experience of each individual. Thus, the participant will have limited opportunity to acquire skills and experience. Probably more important is that he will have limited opportunity to acquire perspective and insight into the process requirements that are inherent in such a situation.

Much of the anxiety and tension arise from the belief that "there must be a better way." One hears over and over the criticism that the operation of the group was inefficient, that it shouldn't have taken so much time and needless effort to complete its work. These observations fail to take into account the inevitable process dynamics, which each group must work out for itself—it cannot adopt a set by applying Robert's Rules of Order. This failure is not surprising because most individuals have little chance to develop the insight through repeated participation in temporary organizations.

This discussion of the problem has attempted to demonstrate that much of the apparent inefficiency and wheel spinning is inherent in the nature of temporary organizations. It reflects the work that must be performed to create the process dynamics necessary for the functioning of the group and the "working out" of the perfectly valid anxiety generated by the severe time pressures and complexity of the assignment. Awareness of the relevance of the "inefficiency" and anxiety can hopefully permit us to function more productively as members of temporary organizations.

16   R & D in a Multinational Firm

The structure and dynamics of western societies seem to dictate the growth of ever larger institutions—be they labor unions, industrial enterprises, churches, educational institutions, or government units. It is now widely believed that in the future we will increasingly see many segments of industry dominated by a relatively few giant corporations whose scope is worldwide and whose operations inevitably become multinational in the total sense of conducting production, sales, distribution, and financing on a worldwide basis. Worldwide cost leadership is already regarded as necessary for competitive survival in many fields. Similarly, the entire world is now regarded as a potential market, both from the point of view of identifying opportunities and anticipating the plans of competitors. Needless to say, technology, as one of the principal weapons in the arsenal of industrial progress, is deeply involved in this trend toward multinational corporations. Both in the sphere of generating new technology and in the application of technology, any firm that has aspirations toward worldwide operation must confront the problem of how to deal with technology in a multinational organization.

As discussions among major powers are now demonstrating, technology has become an instrument of international diplomacy. During the decade of the 1960s it became an important consideration in national domestic policy throughout the world. Because of the unusual demands on multinational firms to be responsive to local government sensibilities, it will be necessary to start this discussion with an examination of the role of technology in government policy and the diffusion of technology across national boundaries. With this as background, this chapter examines the reasons for performing R & D on a multinational scale, some of the difficulties of achieving coordination and technology transfer, and some of the specific managerial problems that must be faced.

To a greater extent than is realized by many people, technology has itself been treated as a commodity for a long time. The worldwide structure of patenting permits technology to be regarded as a proprietary "product," which can be bought and sold just like any other product. Technological exchange agreements between companies in various countries that arrange for the flow of technology from one organization to another and which specify the rights and privileges of the parties to the transaction are now exceedingly common. These agreements, on a worldwide basis, have been one of the most important vehicles for the diffusion of technology from one society to another. That they can be exceedingly useful in the rapid growth of a particular nation has been amply demonstrated in the post-World War II period by the Japanese, who have, to a very substantial extent, relied on technological licenses to give them access to know-how developed elsewhere in the erstwhile more technologically advanced countries of the world.

While these technological licensing arrangements have been recognized for their value in technological diffusion, the limitations that they impose on the receiving country are also increasingly recognized. Typically, these agreements, for understandable reasons, provide protection for the originator of the technology by requiring license-free access to any improvements or extensions of the technology generated by the licensee. For the country aspiring to achieve technological parity, this arrangement has been characterized as running a race between two people with a pole between them. No matter how hard the one behind tries to catch up, all he does is help the one in front run faster. Consequently, governments are recognizing that they must be concerned about the health, vitality, and effectiveness of the domestic mechanisms for generating technology.

Technology and National Policy

Looked at another way, this conclusion simply points out that technology is by now generally recognized throughout the world as one of the forcing functions that provides for growth and vitality in a nation. The traditional instruments of economic growth have been arable land, raw materials, a trained and work-oriented labor force, and availability of adequate and flexible sources of capital. Now a fifth, technology, is joining the foursome, and is even being regarded as one of the primary engines of growth. Those countries possessing ample natural resources increasingly view technology as the critical element in converting themselves from being a supplier of raw materials to becoming a producer of fabricated products. The latter, of course, provides much greater employment opportunities for a labor force. This connection between technology and employment is more and more recognized by the underdeveloped and smaller nations, many of which may have ample raw material resources but find themselves with a very low standard of living for a large population and with a need to increase employment in a fashion that will greatly increase personal income. Only by advancing to the production of finished or semifinished goods can significant employment opportunities be created, and this step can be taken only by increased use of technology.

Thus, technology is increasingly being recognized as an indispensable instrument of national policy. Statements regarding the role of technology and plans to improve its effectiveness and productivity are more or less routinely incorporated into the platforms of political parties. Perhaps even more important is that specific programs are enunciated and enacted by legislative bodies to insure that technology grows at an adequate rate, that it is directed along lines regarded as desirable from the standpoint of national welfare and vitality, and that the practitioners of technology are both properly compensated and adequately responsive to national needs and priorities. Although all these activities are still in a primitive stage, they are becoming matters of concern for every government among the developed countries, and one can expect to see increasing sophistication as additional experience is acquired in the administration of programs and the testing of alternative solutions.

Individual governments are developing specific programs that include tax incentives, special R & D grants, fast write-offs òn R & D equipment and investment in R & D, government participation in risk sharing of technological ventures, and government guidance in the restructure of industry to improve technological competitive position. Both Great Britain and France have encouraged and influenced the restructuring of their computer companies to create more technically viable entities. The Canadian Industrial Research and Development Incentive Act (IRDIA) and

Program to Aid Industrial Technology (PAIT) are designed to provide cash refunds as tax incentives for increased R & D and to extend loans to aid in bringing developments to commercial application.

For similar reasons, the capability of generating technology is recognized as a national resource. Attention is focused on the capability of educational institutions to produce people with the requisite sophistication of training, on the effectiveness of the institutions that generate and apply technology, and on employment opportunities provided for professionals trained in science and engineering. The latter is desirable to insure that they stay in the country. The considerable attention devoted to the "brain drain" during the 1960s is a reflection of the importance of this area. The concern about the brain drain is fundamentally related to the loss of superior people. Individual countries believe they cannot sit idly by and watch a steady attrition of people with superior intellect, creativity, and motivation who move to another nation where more opportunity and reward are offered. Thus, on the one hand, the care and feeding of technology, and on the other hand, the application of technology to national purposes, are recognized matters of concern for governments.

International Character of Technology

Because of these trends, technology in a variety of ways is taking its place along with commerce as one of the major forces for acculturation. It has been one, and may even become the greatest, of the powerful integrating forces among nations. The international character of science has long been recognized. The fact that science speaks a common language throughout the world in terms of the methodologies and terminology used, the theories and techniques that are accepted as valid, and the equipment that is available constitutes a tremendous integrating force. This similarity of language across national boundaries has been instrumental in encouraging communication among scientists and in fostering a feeling of a community of interest among scientists, irrespective of their national origins. Just as powerful a force has been the common system of values that scientists share with respect to the role of knowledge in man's welfare and progress. This sharing of common ideals, of common priorities, and of similar objectives has made science and engineering a truly international community.

The nature of the research and development process itself contributes to this feeling of community because people who are engaged in this activity, as do all professionals, look to their peers for sophisticated appreciation and approbation. As the world has become increasingly specialized, the audience to which one looks for approbation is worldwide because the people who are most closely associated with one's particular interests may be working any place in the world.

Technological Transfer

The manner in which technology is transferred into other countries typically follows a classical pattern. Normally, this process starts with the receiving country importing the product that is based on an advance in technology. The first requirement for the receiving country is to have in place, or to put in place, the capability to apply the product appropriately and to render service for it. Thus, application engineering and customer service become the first steps in the diffusion of technology. After direct importation of the product has demonstrated the market potential, the next phase involves the importation of components or subassemblies, with the final product being assembled in the receiving country. This step helps to provide additional domestic employment, but it involves minimum investment and little technical risk.

The third step typically is for the receiving country to attempt to produce some of the components or subassemblies involved in the final product. While an attempt is made both to make and to justify the choice of components selected for domestic manufacture on the basis of cost effectiveness, the concept of cost tends to be modified by considerations of balance of payments, desire to develop the manufacturing capability of the economy, and national pride. Not infrequently, companies that are operating in a receiving country find themselves under pressure from the local government to undertake both production and assembly of components before the traditional cost analysis can indicate that it is justified. The final stage in this process, of course, is for the receiving country to undertake the production of all or virtually all of the components involved in a particular product, as well as the assembly work. At this stage it will have virtually duplicated the technological capability generated in the host country.

Further extensions of development would involve the receiving country's undertaking additional modification or refinement of the technology, either in response to local market needs that provide outlet for its own creative capabilities or in an attempt to export the product with its accompanying technology into other less developed countries. Providing for local market and production differences is typically the first technical step because almost inevitably a product developed for one economy is not optimum for another. Local customers have different preferences, product standards are frequently different, and changes in the scale of manufacture call for different production methods, which sometimes require changes in materials and design. Once some technical capability has been established, domestic scientists and engineers are certain to see additional opportunities for improvement. There is an almost irresistible creepage from production engineering upstream into design and development. Thus, although the parent company may feel that for reasons of efficiency and standardization it wants technology to originate with the parent, it will likely find it almost impossible to maintain that position. Instead, it faces the far more difficult question of trying to decide how much duplication of technical capability and variation of product is desirable to accept in the interest of stimulating local incentive, taking advantage of local capability, serving local customers, and—perhaps most important of all—placating local governments.

Performing Multinational R & D

This discussion of the transfer of technology has adopted the perspective of the receiving country. A company undertaking multinational operations typically goes through a three-phase sequence. First, it sells its products to international customers simply as a form of market extension, relying on its domestic manufacturing and technological base. This phase, if continued, leads it to establish an international sales and service operation. Second, it builds microcosms of itself in selected foreign countries to undertake production and sale of products together with the necessary technical capability to modify designs to fit local markets and to accommodate to local manufacturing capabilities. Ordinarily the basic technological strength is retained in the parent company and new technology is exported in the form of new products and new designs. The third phase is some form of worldwide rationalization in which the operations of the total company are divided up among all its multinational components. Eventually, worldwide responsibility for selected products is itself parceled out. Not surprisingly, this latter phase is very protracted, and few companies have achieved true worldwide rationalization.

While the initial objective of a country is to become relatively self-sufficient in technology and to achieve virtual parity with other nations, it inexorably progresses to the point of wishing to capitalize on technology as an instrument of international trade. This national posture, of course, reinforces the desires of the technical force in the foreign-owned subsidiary to carve out a larger arena in which to operate. When the relationship, which is initially analogous to the parent-child relationship, evolves toward one of cooperating equals, it becomes almost mandatory for the multinational parent company to rationalize its operations on a worldwide basis. By so doing it can attain the advantages of specialization among its national operations and yet offer the scope of a worldwide market for selected products or components to each national subsidiary. This extension of management philosophy will require great skill and sophistication to implement, and multinational companies are only beginning to go down this path.

Fundamentally, a company undertakes technical work in another country for two reasons: first, to provide technical support for its business in the country, the situation we discussed earlier under technological transfer; and second, to give tangible evidence of meeting its responsibility as a full-fledged corporate citizen in the other country. The discussion above, which emphasized the increasing attention being devoted to technology and its increasing importance as an instrument of national policy, indicates the significance of this latter reason. It is now accepted as a fact of life by truly multinational countries that no matter what the difficulties (discussed below), it is inevitable that if a company indeed wishes to operate on a multinational basis with a full-fledged business presence in selected countries, it must accept the necessity, at some point in the course of events, of placing R & D capability in each country in which it so operates. This requirement is not necessarily accepted with enthusiasm because the difficulties of conducting R & D in a multinational framework are serious, in spite of the fact that science and engineering are regarded as international activities. The normal criteria of efficiency would dictate that such an effort not be undertaken. In fact, the requirement is typically accepted more with resignation than with pleasure.

In addition to these two central reasons, one frequently hears discussion about other advantages that accrue from conducting R & D on a multinational basis; for example, to take advantage of particular capabilities that exist in a given country, to establish better coupling with the science and technology of a given country, or to take advantage of lower costs for performing R & D in some other country. As will be seen below, I believe these objectives are essentially ephemeral compared with the two central reasons for undertaking multinational R & D. In particular, the objective of improved coupling in many cases can be achieved more effectively in other ways. Largely because science is so international in its character, coupling in practice occurs much more effectively when achieved directly between practicing professionals throughout the world than it does by establishing an R & D component in a given country for that purpose. The principal reason for this poor performance is that an R & D establishment in a particular country must inevitably begin to focus its attention on a limited number of fields and within that framework it can perhaps establish very good coupling with the other professionals within the country. On the other hand, other areas of interest to the parent company, outside the areas of specialization in the particular foreign laboratory, tend to receive much less attention; in fact, they are much better covered by professionals in the parent company who are active in those fields. In this same sense, the fact that lower R & D costs exist in a given country does not produce any particular advantage if the R & D results are themselves not used effectively on a worldwide basis; as we will see, there are very serious problems in coupling to R & D output across national borders.

Difficulties in Achieving Coordination

One of the first goals to topple in the operation of a multinational firm is the expectation of having a worldwide integrated program of R & D. It is true that there are some multinational companies, such as Philips, Royal Dutch Shell, and Brown Boveri, that conduct R & D in a multinational framework and which do achieve a certain amount of coherence in their work. However, these companies have attained a level of sophistication in multinational business and a multilingual capability which can be achieved only by decades of effort. Even so, closer examination indicates that their R & D activities on an integrated basis are essentially intra-European in nature. Here the problem of distance is much more manageable. A rough rule of thumb that some follow is that unless an organization is within easy one-day commuting distance of another, it is virtually impossible to maintain an adequate level of integration and coordination. In other words, it must be possible for an individual to get up in the morning, go to the airport, fly to another country, spend the day working there, and return in time to sleep in his own bed, if one is to expect an adequate level of integration.

Where large distances are involved (for example between Europe and the United States), much more limited objectives will have to be established for the coordination of research and development. One manager responsible for coordination on a worldwide basis has used the descriptive term "harmonize" to characterize the limited objective that he seeks in providing integration between technical activities in Europe and in the United States. Managers of these activities seek to create an awareness of the programs and capabilities that exist in the respective laboratories, but they approach each other very much as equals in a large-scale undertaking. They inform each other of intentions and plans but without any requirement to bow to each other's wishes in terms of programs being carried out beyond what is obvious from the internal logic of the programs themselves.

The barriers to transition, which were discussed earlier in terms of organizational separation and physical separation, are amplified dramatically when looking at R & D and the use of R & D results across national borders. In many cases the distance barrier becomes very much greater indeed. In addition to the organizational barrier are added barriers in language, in local customs, and in tradition, which become almost insuperable.

More modest goals for transition and utilization of results must be established and more time and effort devoted to accomplishing transition. In particular, more attention must be paid to insuring that the language barrier is minimized. In spite of the remarkable multilingual facility that many European businessmen and scientists have, they find it necessary to avoid simultaneous linguistic and technical translation. In other words, the transfer of technology from one country to another country must, if at all possible, occur at the same level of science and engineering. Science developed in one country must be diffused to scientists in another country, and then the process of diffusion down through the technical chain into applied research, development, and engineering can occur in the second country. If an attempt is made to transfer scientific results in one country to applied technologists in another country, the barriers of language and culture added to the differences in technical point of view and terminology make the process virtually impossible.

An additional barrier to maintaining a coordinated R & D program on a multinational basis is the obstacle generated by local sensibilities. These can be of two sorts. First, the local technical and commercial organizations quite naturally develop a certain amount of pride in their own existence and their own capability. This makes them eager to take on additional responsibilities, but at the same time resistant to efforts to specialize their role and make them dependent on "foreign" organizations for part of their technology. The desire for self-sufficiency is very deep-rooted particularly when it is accompanied by local national pride that seeks expression in the attainment of autonomy. Extreme care must be exercised in establishing in a country a specialized technical capability that may offend this sense of self-sufficiency. It calls for a high level of trust in relationships to ask an organization in one country to become partially dependent on the technical inputs of an organization in another country.

To this is added, of course, the problem of the local pride associated with nationalism. The growing role assigned to technology in attaining national growth makes individual governments very much concerned about the kind of technology that foreign-owned subsidiaries are developing within the domestic boundaries. Many governments are deeply suspicious that the self-interests of the parent company are not truly aligned with the self-interests of the nation and that, in the interests of efficiency and control, the nation is being shortchanged by attempts to withhold from it the technological capability that has already been developed in another country. The consequence is, of course, to keep it in a subservient position technically, a politically intolerable circumstance. This situation frequently leads to undesirable duplication of effort when viewed in disinterested economic terms. Despite the existence of a perfectly adequate technical capability in the parent company, the multinational firm may find itself under inexorable pressure from a particular nation to establish a domestic R & D capability, even though it is difficult to find programs that are not already being better pursued elsewhere.

In summary, a company aspiring to truly multinational operation—i.e., conducting manufacturing, marketing, and financing operations in another country—will find it necessary to establish some local technical capability. Furthermore, there will be steady pressures to extend the area of technical activity upstream into more advanced R & D work. The converse situation should also be noted: until a full-fledged business entity has been created, there is little point in establishing an advanced technical capability. Firms with long multinational experience are emphatic in stressing that a satellite R & D operation in another country *must* have a viable domestic business operation to serve. Without a contiguous business to serve, the satellite technical group faces a virtually impossible task in defining a viable role for itself in competition with the technology being generated by the parent company.

Establishing a Foreign R & D Activity

The task of establishing an R & D capability in a foreign subsidiary requires skill, patience, and sophisticated understanding of the difficulties that are inherent in such an undertaking. The first steps taken to establish a domestic technical capability in another country must have a strong local flavor. The clear initial objective of the organization must be to provide technical input to the local business so as to improve product service and to aid in application and adaptation to local needs and local preferences. On this foundation can gradually be established, and inevitably will have to be established, additional technical capabilities and activities of a more advanced nature.

Unless there is clear recognition of the serious limitations on effective multinational R & D and a consequent formulation of relatively modest aspirations, disillusionment is almost certain. Companies with extensive experience in this kind of activity recognize that the process of establishing an effective laboratory in another nation will be slow and probably painful. The likelihood is that, irrespective of the care given to planning, a number of mistakes will be made both in staffing and in developing viable philosophy and objectives for the new organization. These latter will have to be evolved over time, partly on the basis of experience and partly on the basis of mutual education among the parties involved in the transaction. Thus, the local populus, the local government, and the local business organization will gradually have to acquire sophistication and skill in working with and using an R & D organization; in turn, the parent company will have to acquire skill, patience, and sophistication in working effectively with nationals in another country.

A third point to be recognized is that a different order of priorities will have to be established in judging effectiveness and performance. In particular, most of the traditional criteria having to do with efficiency will, in effect, have to be deemphasized because, as we have seen, there are many reasons why R & D conducted across national borders will not be efficient by the normal standards of efficiency. Some duplication of effort is unavoidable. Some results will inevitably not be used in another country, even though they are made known to it. Some programs will be undertaken which can be objectively demonstrated to be indefensible from the standpoint of cost and/or not within the capability of the domestic organization. Nevertheless, for the variety of local reasons indicated earlier, such programs will be undertaken on some occasions. On the other hand, the criteria having to do with responsiveness will have to receive a great deal more attention. Responsiveness to the local climate, responsiveness to the local market, responsiveness to the local aspirations of the people involved will become very important factors in determining success.

New Managerial Problems

One frequently unanticipated problem involves the altered character of the manager's job in operating a foreign subsidiary. The "nuts and bolts" activities associated with the problems of conducting R & D or any other kind of activity in another country demand far more time than is generally anticipated when such an operation is established. By "nuts and bolts" I mean such things as salary administration, employee benefits, housing, education for employees' children, arranging transfers, buying property, acquiring licenses and franchises, negotiating tax agreements—many of the activities that are virtually taken for granted when conducting business within the United States. A man transferring from the United States to Europe must decide whether to place his children in the local school or to use a special English language school (which somebody must help him locate and evaluate). He will find that the intricacies of purchasing are very different from those in the United States, and that laws controlling the creation of a business and regulating its conduct differ markedly from country to country. It is the almost universal observation of people involved in multinational activities that far more of a manager's time is devoted to activities of this type than is characteristic of domestic operations.

There are three reasons for this circumstance. First, for reasons of equity, when a company is conducting operations on a multinational scale it has an obligation, insofar as it possibly can, to insure equitable treatment among people as they move from one country to another. Otherwise, it will find itself creating its own barriers to the transfer of people between countries. The concept of equity becomes a very elusive and subtle thing when there are sophisticated differences in tax structure, in incomes, in cost of living, in availability of perquisites, in cultural elements, etc. Second, there are, of course, the objective differences in ways of doing business: different standards, different procedures, different people to deal with, different laws, different codes of ethics. These differences must be identified and accommodated to, and the process takes time and effort.

The third difference is perhaps more sensitive to deal with, but is one that must be recognized. It is generally accepted that societies differ in a wide variety of ways that involve their entire socioeconomic infrastructure. These differences include everything from the time required to place a phone call, to the problems involved in buying property, to the delays created at border crossings, to differences in the speed with which transportation moves. The cumulative impact affects lead times needed for purchasing, requirements for inventories of supplies, the availability of sophisticated equipment or specialized materials, etc. Factors such as these differ more or less in direct proportion to the level of economic development of the country itself, with the standard of living it has achieved, and with the level of sophistication attained in the technology being used. All of these interlocking circumstances will lead to a considerably slower pace and lower level of achievement compared with the expectations of the typical American businessman or manager of research and development.

What of the Future?

As one looks to the future, one is tempted to ask: "What are the possibilities for removing some of these barriers that currently make multinational R & D a relatively unattractive proposition?" It is apparent that two trends will in the long run help to relieve this situation. The first is the worldwide rationalization mentioned earlier. As the size of operations on a wide-area basis grows, it may become increasingly possible to assign worldwide responsibility for a particular product or group of products to a given foreign operation or, in turn, to assign a segment of the total world market for a variety of products to a given foreign operation. It is apparent, as one observes foreign laboratories of multinational concerns, that they are most successful when they achieve a relatively autonomous role of their own. This same situation, of course, has been apparent in the operation of laboratories in this country. To the extent that the foreign laboratory is a microscopic version of the parent laboratory back home, in every case forced to be small and second class, it almost inevitably will be ineffective. But to the extent that it can be handed its own assignment and achieve a feeling of autonomy and capability in a sphere of technical responsibility, it will achieve a kind of self-awareness and self-pride that will make it a much more effective operation.

The second consideration is that as one views the continuing trend toward the need for worldwide cost leadership, one can look far in the future to the day when sourcing decisions will indeed be made on a worldwide basis. The worldwide capability for, and acceptance of, this necessary step is slowly being developed. Truly multinational operations are growing in Japan and western Europe as well as in the United States, and improvements in transportation and communication are greatly expanding the horizons of a multitude of people. One could begin to say that the word "foreign" is slowly losing its meaning. Nationalism is by no means dead, but rational economic criteria *are* being applied more extensively and with much greater sophistication. Large-scale movements tend to develop their own internal logic, which forces the external world to accommodate so that what was once impossible eventually seems inevitable and natural. If one adopts the time perspective of a historian, one might say that the trend to multinational operation gives evidence of beginning to create such forces. This same drive of internal logic will also undoubtedly lead multinational technology in directions that nobody has yet anticipated.

17

Where Do We Go From Here?

This book opened with a contradiction—a proposition that, whether we realize it or not, we are in the process of trying to institutionalize the creation of change in large corporations by creating a special function for that purpose. It ends with a paradox—R & D, the activity that has been the chief proponent of change, which has been most identified with the creation of continuing change, will achieve the full success it seeks only if it, too, is able to change. In fact, R & D has already begun to be a victim of the forces it has been helping to create; R & D is receiving a dose of its own medicine – change.

Much of the discussion in this book has been an exploration of some of the changes that are needed in R & D and in the milieu in which it operates, if it is to fulfill its destiny. Included in these are changes in behavior, in planning, in transitioning outputs, in communication, and (most vital of all) in perception of its relationship to the rest of the corporation. These additional changes also affect corporate executives. Let us recapitulate the themes developed previously and speculate about additional changes that the coming years will generate.

Can change be institutionalized? Change almost inevitably involves challenge and struggle, threat and opportunity. If we are to institutionalize change, we must institutionalize struggle or combat, insure that it occurs, and yet establish safeguards against its degenerating into destructive war-

fare. As Konrad Lorenz[120] has shown through his studies of aggressive behavior in animals and his challenging analogies to human behavior, combat can play a useful constructive role if it is ritualized; i.e., in human
terms, if people know what the purpose of the contest is, if they recognize
the roles of the contestants, and if all parties to the struggle understand
the rules of combat.

This book has attempted to illuminate some of the things that need to be
done to establish the conditions for constructive combat between those
charged with the effective daily operation of a business, namely, its stewards and those charged with perceiving and bringing into existence the
changes necessary to preserve the long-term viability of the enterprise, i.e.,
the agents of change.

The book began by urging R & D managers to move beyond a self-
limiting role emphasizing advocacy for a fledgling function to one stressing
integration of all elements for creating change into the fabric of the enterprise. This move requires understanding of the pressures felt by the general
executive and recognition of the problems he faces in supporting R & D. It
also requires coming to understand the different kinds of inputs R & D
creates—demand-induced and supply-pushed—and the need for a creative
tension between the two within the R & D component. Conversely, the R &
D input will not be effectively coupled unless the R & D component is
properly organized with respect to the rest of the corporation. This coupling must recognize the need for people with a "futures" responsibility in *all*
functions if innovation is to proceed, and even more it must acknowledge
the requirement for the parent organization to give explicit recognition to
time as a factor in assigning responsibility for planning and decision making.
Unless people are charged with explicit responsibility for "making the case
for the future," the exigencies of the present will always drive out attention
to the future. This assignment for the future must cut across all functions
because successful innovation requires careful orchestration of many
specialties under conditions of considerable stress and uncertainty. R & D
cannot go it alone.

Perhaps the biggest barrier to effective integration is the absence of
methodologies that permit the business executive to incorporate the role of
technology into his strategic planning and to specify the inputs needed from
R & D. Concurrently, R & D managers have lacked the tools to develop
their strategies in terms and concepts consistent with business planning. In
order to deal with this problem, I proposed a matrix form of planning that

relates a spectrum of strategic business options (harvest, grow, extend, or diversify) to a spectrum of technical inputs stated in terms of increasing risk (apply the state-of-the-art, extend the state-of-the-art, develop new technology to supplant old, and invent a new function).

This emphasis on application is then extended into strategic planning for R & D by proposing the use of a classification system that relates the outputs of R & D to the way in which they will be used, whether by product, process, business component, or what have you. For these classifications, one should develop criterion screens that indicate the leverage technical success would produce against the likelihood of achieving success. While the factors to be taken into account are generally applicable (for example, size and rate of growth of the market, likely market share attainable, sensitivity to technology, etc.), it is important that the criterion definitions and algorithms for their use be developed by the local management.

Although improved coupling in planning is indispensable, the payoff comes from the profitable use of R & D output in operations. The transition to operations (technology transfer) requires effective coupling of quite a different character. We have considered the advantages and disadvantages of decentralized versus centralized organizations and explained the popularity of a mixed mode except where the total business had great technical homogeneity.

Beyond the general subject of organization, we must consider specific modes for achieving transition. Here, the original "barriers and bonds" concepts of Jack Morton have been extended to include flexible imaginative control of financial resources as a way to encourage transition. Also advocated is the flexible use and transfer of people to insure that communication remains effective and that some of the enthusiasm and commitment to the innovation are retained at every step in the movement to commercial application.

The key role of communication in achieving effective coupling has been explored from two quite different perspectives. First, with respect to technical communication among professionals, stress has been placed on the interdependence between formal and informal communication. Particular attention has been directed to the vital, but frequently overlooked, role of formal communication in creating the network within which informal communication could occur subsequently. Second, we have explored some of the barriers in perception and values which impede effective communication between technical people and business executives.

Where Do We Stand?

As I noted at the beginning of the book, the creation of a new institution takes a lot of time. The arguments I have been putting forth are not an explication of the present attitudes, behavior, or modes of a majority of either R & D managers or corporate executives. As one would expect in a situation that is very much in a state of flux, different people acquire new perceptions at different rates, and a coherent view of the overall situation is hard to establish. This book is intended to help generate such coherence and to provide some management tools for more effective action.

Recognition of the need to move toward more integration between R & D and the sponsoring enterprise is emerging, but the modes of interaction and the management tools for achieving it are at present sadly lacking. Recognition of the need for a *multifunctional* "futures" component is even more embryonic. Much more attention is being given to the problem of obtaining effective use of R & D outputs, and some managers with vision and imagination are inventing new ways of doing so. Jack Morton's contributions in this area have been particularly important.

Fortunately, continuing exposure and the relentless pressure to establish more effective relationships do have a way of creating improvements in communication. As people with backgrounds in R & D move into general management, and as managers in other functions grow up seeing technology used more effectively, we can expect continuing improvements in communications.

External changes, which for different reasons have forced both large corporations and the technical community to reexamine their values and priorities, may well nurture improved communication. The recent decrease in support for R & D and the severe questioning of the role and contribution of technology to our society have clearly stimulated much reappraisal among scientists and engineers. Out of this is emerging a heightened sense of reponsibility for a more immediate contribution to solving some of our society's major problems. Conversely, there appears to be somewhat less enthusiasm for research whose relevance is remote—at least within the time scale of most mortals. Thus, the businessman's preoccupation with effective application may seem somewhat less foreign.

At the same time, large corporations are finding themselves forced to respond to new standards for safety, for the ecological burden their operations and products generate, and for the second- and third-order consequences of their decisions and actions. They are also having to contemplate a future in which energy and raw materials will be more expensive and less certain of supply. Under these circumstances the definition of profit requires a more sophisticated determination of cost on a much longer time scale. Despite the present uproar by the antitechnologists, I predict that executives will discover that R & D and the insights, adaptability, and rigorous thought of technical people will be a major resource in adapting the corporation to these external forces.

The Challenge of a Mixed Strategy

The big challenge of the next decade, in my view, will derive from the subtle changes involved in the shift from the advocate's role for R & D managers, reinforced by trends emerging among nations as they reach new stages of development in their use of technology. Let me explain this odd juxtaposition of forces.

A shift from an advocate's role implies among other things an ability to view technology and R & D itself in a more detached fashion. Remember, our senior executives are bombarded with special pleading and they see their mission as making resource allocation decisions dispassionately. They usually don't care where their technology comes from, as long as they acquire it as inexpensively as possible. They recognize, even insist, that no company can or should generate all the technology it needs. The goal should be to generate (make) that which will have the greatest leverage by virtue of the competitive advantage it provides, and to buy or otherwise obtain the rest through licensing, acquisition, reliance on vendors, etc. The problem is that the criteria for making such make/buy evaluations have not yet been generated. Executives quite naturally believe they should and must be able to turn to their R & D managers for help in making such judgments because nobody else has the requisite knowledge. This ability to view technology dispassionately as a commodity to be purchased or manufactured is clearly antithetical from the perspective of an advocate.

Thus, the shift toward integration, which we have been urging, is timely. Our discussion of the role of technology in business strategy has emphasized that businesses have been quite successful in strategies based on technical leadership and in strategies requiring the company to follow technically. This discussion is now suggesting an increasing need to learn how to implement a mixed strategy of leading selectively through in-house efforts, while relying on external technology in other areas.

The implementation of such a strategy will require skill and objectivity on the part of R & D management. Success in the pursuit of a leadership strategy in which one seeks to "make" technology requires the development of an esprit de corps based on pioneering work. It develops the kind of pride that regards a successful external development as a challenge to be exceeded, and fosters a powerful NIH factor. This environment is hostile to nurturing the idea that purchasing technology can be the appropriate course of action. Conversely, a strategy that emphasizes following technically by buying technology is not easily converted to a mixed strategy. A technical follower places great emphasis on rapid response and on being very market-oriented. He does not seek or foster the development of people who want to do pioneering technical work. The prospect of such an undertaking is likely to be viewed with some anxiety, and the longer time scale required for such work to pay off may well lead to severe management casualties in both R & D and in the business before the necessary management education and accommodation to a new style have been accomplished.

It is likely that on a much smaller scale we will have to repeat the historical sequence that R & D has gone through. This new responsibility—whether it be to develop the basis for and to implement the purchase of technology in a company which has heretofore sought leadership or to undertake pioneering technical work in a company which heretofore has bought technology—will have to be compartmentalized and protected from the traditional ongoing technical activities.

As indicated above, this trend toward the development and implementation of a mixed strategy will be reinforced by forces at work at the national level in different countries as they evolve more sophisticated national policies with respect to R & D and the use of technology.

The widespread utilization of technical licensing agreements, mentioned in Chapter 16, generates a gradual closing of the "gap" between the licensor nation and the licensee nation. As more licensing agreements are established and as more of the present state-of-the-art is placed in application, the purchasing country begins to encounter the barriers of the present frontiers of technology and thus discovers that needed technology is not always available by licensing from any source. It is then confronted with the dilemma of relegating itself permanently to a technically inferior position (an option likely to impede its continued growth) or of learning how to be a generator of new technology. The change in point of view is profound. Not only is the psychological risk both larger and different in character, but also the management skills and style needed to succeed are greatly different.

The Japanese have demonstrated that following technically can be an enormously successful strategy if one is in the position of catching up, and if one is exceedingly adept in perceiving market opportunities and in developing products to serve them. The United States has demonstrated·that leading technically can also be enormously successful. It is likely in the decade ahead that the great management challenge in both countries will again be in learning how to follow a mixed strategy. With the present scale of technology development and the magnitude of worldwide effort, no country (much less any company) can aspire to technological leadership on all fronts. The criteria for deciding where one should lead and where one should follow have not yet been worked out, nor has there been any practice acquired in applying the criteria.

Thus the paradox: After being the vigorous, aggressive champion of change for others, R & D must itself learn how to change. It must move from autonomy to integration. It may even need to submerge its identity in a multifunctional futures component dedicated to creating those innovations required to maintain the viability of the large corporation. By retaining less visibility and less independence, it may well discover that it has acquired greater influence on, and status in, the corporation it has been striving to change.

Bibliography

Helpful references to material presented in the book frequently apply to more than one chapter. To reduce confusing multiple references, the chapters have been grouped into closely related topics for purposes of designating reference material.

Chapter 1

1. Brooks, Harvey. "Applied Science and Technological Progress: A Report to the Committee on Science and Astronautics, U.S. House of Representatives." The National Academy of Sciences, Washington, D.C., May 25, 1967.
2. Brooks, Harvey. *The Government of Science.* Cambridge, Mass.: M.I.T. Press, 1968.
3. Brown, Harrison. *The Challenge of Man's Future.* New York: Viking, 1954.
4. Bush, Vannevar. *Endless Horizons.* Washington, D.C.: Public Affairs Press, 1946.
5. Conant, James Bryant. *Modern Science & Modern Man.* New York: Columbia University Press, 1952.
6. Conant, James Bryant. *On Understanding Science: An Historical Approach.* New Haven: Yale University Press, 1947.
7. Conant, James Bryant. *Science and Common Sense.* New Haven: Yale University Press, 1951.

8. Cooper, A.C. "R&D Is More Efficient in Small Companies." *Harvard Business Review* (May-June 1964), pp. 75–83.

9. Gardner, John. *Self-Renewal.* Evanston, Ill.: Harper, 1963.

10. Jewkes, John, David Sauers, and Richard Stillerman. *The Sources of Invention.* New York: St. Martin's Press, 1958.

11. Johnson, J.H. (Ed.). "Survival and Growth: The Small R&D Firm." Proceedings of the First National Conference Dealing with the Problems of the Small Firms in the Research & Development Industry. Washington, D.C.: Center for the Study of Private Enterprise, The American University, June 12-14, 1972.

12. Kuhn, Thomas S. *The Structure of Scientific Revolutions.* Chicago: University of Chicago Press, 1962.

13. Machlup, Fritz. *The Production & Distribution of Knowledge in the United States.* Princeton, N.J.: Princeton University Press, 1962.

14. National Science Foundation. *National Patterns of R&D Resources Funds & Manpower in the United States,* 1953–1974, NSF 74–304.

15. National Science Foundation. *Science Indicators 1972, Report of the National Science Board 1973.*

16. Price, Derek J. *Little Science, Big Science.* New York: Columbia University Press, 1963.

17. Rothschild, Lord. "A Framework for Government Research and Development, the Organization of Government R&D," Lord Rothschild, Head of the Central Policy Review Staff. London: Her Majesty's Stationery, November 1971.

Chapters 2, 3, 4, 5

18. Battelle Columbus Laboratories. *Interactions of Science & Technology in the Innovative Process: Some Case Studies.* March 19, 1973.

19. Cooper, A.C. "R&D Is More Efficient in Small Firms," *Harvard Business Review* (May-June 1969), pp. 75–83.

20. Forrester, J. "Common Foundations Underlying Engineering and Management," *IEEE Spectrum* (September 1964).

21. Gruber, William A., and D.G. Marquis. *Factors in the Transfer of Technology.* Cambridge: M.I.T. Press, 1969.

22. Innis, H.A. *Minerva's Owl.* University of Toronto Press, 1948.

23. Jasinski, F.J. "Adapting Organization to New Technology," *Harvard Business Review,* Vol. 37, No. 1 (Jan.-Feb. 1959), pp. 79–86.

24. Kelly, J. "Making Conflict Work for You," *Harvard Business Review*, Vol. 48, No. 4 (July-Aug. 1970), pp. 103–113.

25. Kuhn, Thomas S. *The Structure of Scientific Revolutions*. Chicago: University of Chicago Press, 1962.

26. Kubie, Laurence. *Neurotic Distortion of the Creative Process*. New York: Noonday Press, 1961, p. 213.

27. Lawrence, P.R., and J.W. Lorsch. *Organization and Environment: Managing Differentiation and Integration*, Harvard Business School, Boston, 1967.

28. Lorsch, J.W., and P.R. Lawrence. "Organizing for Product Innovation," *Harvard Business Review*, Vol. 43, No. 2 (Jan.-Feb. 1965), pp. 109–122.

29. Morton, Jack Andrew. *Organizing for Innovation: A Systems Approach to Technical Management*. New York: McGraw-Hill, 1971, pp. 62–72.

30. Myers, S., and D. Marquis. *Successful Industrial Innovations*. National Science Foundation, NSF 69–71.

31. Pelz, Donald C. "Organizational Factors in Creativity," *Innovation*, No. 9 (1970), pp. 2–12.

32. Roe, Ann. *Making of a Scientist*. New York: (Dodd, Mead, 1953); paperback ed., Apollo, 1959.

33. Schon, Donald A. *Technology and Change; the New Heraclitus*. New York: Delacorte Press, 1967.

34. Schon, Donald A. "The Fear of Innovation," *International Science & Technology* (November 1966), pp. 70–78.

35. Schrage, H. "The R&D Entrepreneur: Profile of Success," *Harvard Business Review*, Vol. 43, No. 6 (Nov.-Dec. 1965), pp. 56–69.

36. Steiner, Gary (Ed.). *The Creative Organization*, Chicago: University of Chicago Press, 1965.

37. "Success & Failure in Industrial Innovation," Report on Project Sappho by the Science Policy Research Unit, University of Sussex, published by the Center for the Study of Industrial Innovation, 162 Regent Street, London W 1B 60D.

38. *The Economist*, February 27, 1971, "Behind the Glamour" (Special Insert p. VII-XXXVII).

39. Toffler, Alvin. *Future Shock*, New York: Random House, 1970. (See especially, Part 5: "The Limits of Adaptability."

Chapters 6, 7, 8, 9

40. "Analytical Methods in Government," *Science Policy*. OECD, Paris, 1972.

41. Ansoff, H.I., and J.M. Stewart. "Strategies for a Technology-Based Busi-

ness," *Harvard Business Review*, Vol. 45, No. 6 (Nov.-Dec. 1967).

42. Ayres, Robert W. *Technological Forecasting & Long Range Planning*. New York: McGraw-Hill, 1969.

43. Bower, J.L. *Managing the Resource Allocation Process: A Study of Corporate Planning and Investment*. Boston: Harvard Business School, 1970.

44. Bright, J.R. "Opportunity & Threat in Technological Change," *Harvard Business Review*. Vol. 42, No. 6 (Nov.-Dec. 1963), pp. 76–86.

45. Bright, J.R. *Technological Forecasting for Industry and Government*. Englewood Cliffs, N.J.: Prentice-Hall, 1968.

46. Drucker, P.F. "Twelve Fables of Research Management," *Harvard Business Review*, Vol. 41, No. 1 (Jan.-Feb. 1963), pp. 103–108.

47. Hirsch, I., W. Milwitt, and W.J. Oakes. "Increasing the Productivity of Scientists," *Harvard Business Review*, Vol. 36, No. 2 (March-April 1958), pp. 66–76.

48. Jantsch, E. *Technological Forecasting in Perspective*. OECD, Paris, 1967.

49. Jay, Antony. *Management and Machiavelli: An Inquiry into the Politics of Corporate Life*. New York: Holt, Rinehart and Winston, 1967.

50. Johnson, S.C., and C. Jones. "How to Organize for New Products," *Harvard Business Review*, Vol. 35, No. 3 (May-June 1957), pp. 49–62.

51. Kuhn, Thomas S. "The Essential Tension: Tradition and Innovation in Scientific Research," in Calvin W. Taylor and Frank Barron (Eds.), *Scientific Creativity: Its Recognition and Development*. New York: Wiley, 1963, pp. 341–354.

52. Kuhn, Thomas S. *The Structure of Scientific Revolutions*. Chicago: University of Chicago Press, 1962.

53. Levitt, T. "Creativity Is Not Enough," *Harvard Business Review*, Vol. 41, No. 3 (May-June 1963), pp. 53–60.

54. Levitt, T. "Marketing Myopia," *Harvard Business Review*, Vol. 38, No. 4 (July-Aug. 1960), pp. 45–56.

55. McGlauchlin, L.E. "Long Range Technical Planning," *Harvard Business Review*, Vol. 46, No. 4 (July-Aug. 1968), pp. 54–64.

56. Miller, R.W. "How to Plan and Control with PERT," *Harvard Business Review*, Vol. 40, No. 2 (March-April 1962).

57. Quinn, J.B., and R.M. Cavanaugh. "Fundamental Research Can Be Planned," *Harvard Business Review*, Vol. 42, No. 2 (Jan.-Feb. 1964), pp. 111–124.

58. Quinn, J.B. "How to Evaluate Research Output," *Harvard Business Review*, Vol. 38, No. 2 (March-April 1960), pp. 67–80.

59. Quinn, J.B. "Long Range Planning of Industrial Research," *Harvard Business Review*, Vol. 39, No. 4 (July-Aug. 1961).

60. Quinn, J.B. *Yardsticks for Industrial Research: The Evaluation of Research and Development Output.* New York: Ronald Press, 1959.

61. Roberts, E. *The Dynamics of Research and Development.* New York: Harper & Row, 1964.

62. *Service to Management, Trends in Research and Development,* RL 20501, Arthur D. Little, Inc.

63. Tilles, S. "How to Evaluate Corporate Strategy," *Harvard Business Review,* Vol. 42, No. 4 (July-Aug. 1963), pp. 111–121.

64. Tilles, S. "Strategies for Allocating Funds," *Harvard Business Review,* Vol. 44, No. 1 (Jan.-Feb. 1966), pp. 72–80.

65. *The Analysis of Research and Development in Ministry of Technology,* Programmes Analysis Unit, United Kingdom, PAO, March 1967.

66. "The Planning-Programming-Budgeting System: Progress and Potentials," Report of the Subcommittee on Economy in Government of the Joint Economic Committee, Congress of the United States, December 1967.

Chapter 10

67. Barnard, C.I. *The Functions of the Executive.* Cambridge: Harvard University Press, 1953.

68. Jay, Antony. *Management and Machiavelli: An Inquiry into the Politics of Corporate Life.* New York: Holt, Rinehart and Winston, 1967.

69. March, J.G., and H.A. Simon. *Organizations.* New York: John Wiley, 1958; London: Chapman & Hall.

70. Mees, C.E.K., and J.A. Leermakers. *The Organization of Industrial Scientific Research.* New York: McGraw-Hill, 1950.

71. Stanley, A.O., and K.K. White. *Organizing the R&D Function.* New York: American Management Association, 1965.

Chapter 11

72. Gruber, W.H., and D.G. Marquis. *Factors in the Transfer of Technology.* Cambridge: M.I.T. Press, 1969.

73. Illinois Institute of Technology. *TRACES: Technology in Retrospect and Critical Events in Science.* Chicago: IIT Research Inst., 1968, 1969, vols. 1 and 2.

74. Langrish, J. "Innovation in Industry. Some Results of the Queen's Award Study," Research Report No. 15, University of Manchester, September 1969.

75. Morton, J.A. *Organizing for Innovation; A Systems Approach to Technical Management.* New York: McGraw-Hill, 1971.
76. OECD, "The Conditions for Success in Technological Innovation." Paris, 1970.
77. Peterson, R.W. "New Venture Management in a Large Company," *Harvard Business Review,* Vol. 45, No. 3 (May-June 1967), pp. 68–76.
78. Quinn, J.B., and J.A. Meuller. "Transferring Research Results to Operations," *Harvard Business Review,* Vol. 41, No. 1 (Jan.-Feb. 1963), pp. 49–66.
79. Schon, D.A. *Technology and Change: The New Heraclitus.* New York: Delacorte Press, 1967.
80. "Success & Failure in Industrial Innovation," Report on Project Sappho by the Science Policy Research Unit, University of Sussex. Published by the Center for the Study of Industrial Innovation, 162 Regent Street, London W 1B 60D.

Chapters 12, 13

81. Allen, Thomas J. "Information Flow in Research & Development Laboratories," *Administrative Science Quarterly,* Vol. 14, No. 1, pp. 12–19.
82. Allen, Thomas J. "Performance of Information Channels in the Transfer of Technology," *M.I.T. Conference on Human Factors in the Transfer of Technology,* Cambridge, Mass., May 1966.
83. Allen, T.J., A. Gerstenfeld, and P.G. Gerstberger. "The Problem of Internal Consulting in Research and Development Organizations," *Working Paper–Alfred P. Sloan School of Management,* Cambridge, #319–68, July 1968.
84. Allen, T.J. "The Utilization of Information Sources During R&D Proposal Preparation," *Working Paper–Alfred P. Sloan School of Management,* Cambridge, #97–64, October 1964.
85. Allen, T.J., M.P. Andrien, Jr., and A. Gerstenfeld. "Time Allocation Among Three Technical Information Channels by R&D Engineers," *Working Paper–Alfred P. Sloan School of Management,* Cambridge, #184–66, April 1966.
86. Hall, Edward T. *The Silent Language.* New York: Doubleday, 1959.
87. Haystrom, W.O. *The Scientific Community.* New York: Basic Books, 1965.
88. Hill, Karl (Ed.). *The Management of Scientists,* Boston: Beacon Press, 1969.
89. Kubie, Laurence. *Neurotic Distortion of the Creative Process.* New York: Noonday Press, 1961, p.213.

90. Marcson, Simon. *The Scientist in American Industry.* New York: Harper, 1960.

91. Pelz, Donald C., and Frank M. Andrews. *Scientists in Organizations: Productive Climates for Research & Development.* New York: Wiley, 1966.

91A. Snow, C.P. *The Two Cultures and the Scientific Revolution.* New York: Cambridge University Press, 1959.

Chapters 14, 15

92. Ansoff, H.I. "The Firm of the Future," *Harvard Business Review, Vol. 43, No. 5 (Sept.-Oct. 1965), pp. 163–178.*

93. Argyris, C. *Integrating the Individual and the Organization.* New York: John Wiley, 1964.

94. Bales, R.F., and F.L. Strodtbeck. "Phases in Group Problem Solving," *Journal of Abnormal and Social Psychology,* Vol. 46 (1951), pp. 485–495.

95. Bennis, Warren G. *Changing Organizations.* New York: McGraw-Hill, 1966.

96. Bennis, Warren G. *The Temporary Society.* New York: Harper & Row, 1968.

97. Berkowitz, L. "Sharing Leadership in Small Decision-Making Groups," *Journal of Abnormal & Social Psychology,* Vol. 48 (1953), pp. 231–238.

98. Cartwright, D., and A. Zander. *Group Dynamics: Research & Theory,* 3d ed. New York: Harper & Row, 1968.

99. Crockett, W.H. "Emerging Leadership in Small Decision-Making Groups," *Journal of Abnormal & Social Psychology,* Vol. 51 (1955), pp. 378–383.

100 Deutsch, Morton, and Robert M. Krauss. *Theories in Social Psychology.* New York: Basic Books, 1965.

101. Kornhauser, W. *Scientists in Industry: Conflict and Accommodation.* Berkeley: University of California Press, 1962.

102. Leavitt, H., and T.L. Whistler. "Management in the 1980's," *Harvard Business Review,* Vol. 36, No. 6 (Nov.-Dec. 1958), pp. 41–48.

103. Maslow, A.H. *Motivation and Personality.* New York: Harper & Row, 1954.

104. McGregor, D. *The Human Side of Enterprise.* New York: McGraw-Hill, 1960.

105. Middleton, C.J. "How to Set Up a Project Organization," *Harvard Business Review,* Vol. 45, No. 2 (March-April 1967), pp. 73–82.

106. Orth, C.D., J.C. Bailey, and F.W. Wolek. *Administering Research & Development: The Behavior of Scientists and Engineers in Organizations,* Homewood, Ill.: Richard D. Irwin & Co., 1964.

107. Wickesberg, A.K., and T.C. Cronin. "Management by Task Force," *Harvard Business Review,* Vol. 40, No. 6 (Nov.-Dec. 1962), pp. 111–118.

Chapter 16

108. Brooks, Harvey. "What's Happening to the U.S. Lead in Technology?," *Harvard Business Review (May-June 1972)*.
109. OECD, *Gaps in Technology*. Paris, 1968.
110. Quinn, J.B. "Technological Competition: Europe vs. U.S.," *Harvard Business Review*, Vol. 44, No. 4 (July-Aug. 1966), pp. 113–130.
111. Servan-Schreiber, J.-J. *The American Challenge*. New York: Avon, 1967.
112. Vernon, Raymond. *Sovereignty at Bay: The Multinational Spread of U.S. Enterprises*. New York: Basic Books, 1971.
113. Vernon, Raymond (Ed.). *The Technology Factor in International Trade*. New York: Columbia University Press, 1970.
114. Yoshino, M.Y. *Japan's Managerial System: Tradition and Innovation*. Cambridge: M.I.T. Press, 1968.

Chapter 17

115. Battelle Columbus Laboratories. *Science, Technology, & Innovation*. Columbus, 1973.
116. Brooks, Harvey. "Can Science Survive in the Modern Age," *Science* Vol. 174 (Jan. 10, 1971).
117. Brooks, Harvey. *The Government of Science*, Cambridge: M.I.T. Press, 1968.
118. *Daedalus*, "Toward the Year 2000: Work in Progress," (Summer 1967).
119. Gardner, John. *Self-Renewal*. Evanston, Ill.: Harper, 1963.
120. Lorenz, Konrad. *On Aggression*. New York: Harcourt, Brace & World, 1963.
121. Starr, Chauncey. "Technology Assessment & National Policy," *OECD Seminar on Technology Assessment*, Paris, Jan. 26-28, 1972.

General

122. Mansfield, Edwin. *The Economics of Technological Change*. New York: Norton, 1968.
123. Nelson, R.R. (Ed.). *The Rate and Direction of Inventive Activity*. Princeton, N.J.: Princeton University Press, 1962.
124. Schmoockler, Jacob. *Invention and Economic Growth*. Cambridge: Harvard University Press, 1966.

Index